ESSAY IN PHYSICS

BY THE SAME AUTHOR

Liberalism: Its Principles and Proposals, 1902

Philosophy and the Ordinary Man, 1932

Practical Ethics, 1935

Belief and Action: An Everyday Philosophy, 1937

An Unknown Land, 1942

Memoirs, 1945

A Book of Quotations, 1947

Creative Man and Other Addresses, 1949

Essay in Physics

HERBERT L. SAMUEL

(Viscount Samuel)

Hon. D.C.L. (*Oxford*) Hon. LL.D. (*Cambridge and Liverpool*)

President of the Royal Institute of Philosophy

WITH A LETTER FROM Dr. Albert Einstein

HARCOURT, BRACE AND COMPANY *NEW YORK*

PRINTED IN THE UNITED STATES OF AMERICA

Foreword

This book deals with matters lying in the province where physics and philosophy meet and overlap. Not being myself a physicist, and approaching these problems primarily from the philosophic side, I asked several scientists of my acquaintance if they would be good enough to give me their help by reading the Essay in draft and letting me have their comments and criticisms. This they readily did and sent me a number of suggestions for omissions, expansions, and amendments which I have gratefully adopted. In particular I would offer my acknowledgements to Dr. E. N. da C. Andrade, Professor Herbert Dingle, Sir Richard Gregory, Professor A. V. Hill, Sir Ben Lockspeiser, Sir Henry Tizard, Dr. G. J. Whitrow, and Professor Sir Edmund Whittaker for their valuable help.

In many respects this book does not follow present trends in physics and may therefore prove controversial. I cite those eminent names only in order to express my thanks and not in any degree as invoking their authority in support of the propositions and arguments put forward. These scientists have of course not been asked to sponsor this book either as a whole or in any part. If it is to be criticized as heterodox it must stand on its own feet and speak for itself.

This foreword was intended to end there, but now something more must be added.

A friendship of long standing allowed me to send to Dr. Albert Einstein a copy of this book in proof, in the hope that he might read it and let me have his opinion. This he has been good enough to do, sending me a comment, from the standpoint of Relativity Theory, on the principal matter dealt with in the first part of this essay. Although his letter was not written with a view to publication, anything from Einstein's pen, upon the root problems of physics which are in constant debate among philosophers and scientists, must be of general interest. I therefore asked, and have received, his permission to include his letter in this little book. Without adding any further comments of my own, I would express to him my warmest thanks.

S.

November, 1950

Note This book was first published in England in February, 1951. The present edition includes an additional section on The Theory of an Expanding Universe, and a few minor additions and corrections here and there.

S.

August, 1951

CONTENTS

ESSAY IN PHYSICS

I. Nature and Mathematics

1

Curiosity is the first step to discovery. The child inquires about the things around him. The adult mind contemplates the sun, moon, and stars and wonders at them. The student explores the knowledge accumulated by mankind. So arise philosophy, science, and religion, and all the intellectual and practical activities of civilized man. "First doubt, then inquire, then discover; that," said Buckle, "has been the process with all our great thinkers."

Curiosity stimulated imagination, and the two together, loose from reason, gave birth to all kinds of fantasies and figments. Primitive peoples drew no hard line between fancy and fact: fairies and devils, magic and incantations, found ready belief. Afterwards came philosophy, which, although exalting reason, itself invented elaborate systems of fictional abstractions. It imagined 'qualities,' 'principles,' 'essences,' 'categories,' and the like, and gave these as the causes of all the phenomena of matter and of mind. The fortunes of men and of nations were supposed to be determined by some undefined external force which was termed 'chance,' 'destiny,' or sometimes 'history.'

Then came natural science, with its processes of observation, experiment, measurement, calculation, prediction, and verification. These proved wonderfully effective: during the last three hundred years the successes of science have transformed civilization. Under these influences, philosophy has discarded many of its old figments—although not a few remain, for the bewilderment of mankind.

But now, in this first half of the twentieth century, there has been a surprising inversion of the roles of philosophy and science. While philosophy, under the influence of empirical science, is no longer concentrating so much upon metaphysics, but is turning more to the search for the causes of natural phenomena and of human actions—at this very time physics, fundamental among the sciences, is tending to revert to ideas not unlike those of the old Schoolmen, which philosophy, since the time of Francis Bacon, has been at pains to discard.

2

During this period, and increasingly in recent years, the greatest triumphs of physicists have been won with the help of mathematics. They have devised mathematical methods of exquisite ingenuity, which have enabled them to probe much farther than ever before into the recesses of nature. These achievements culminated in the discovery of the structure of matter and in the formulation of the principles of relativity and of quantum mechanics.

So successful has been the combination of observation and experiment with measurement and calculation that most physicists of the present day have come to believe that this line of approach is the only one worth pursuing. Many go so far as to hold that what cannot be humanly observed and physically measured must be regarded as scientifically unknown; and what is unknown, if it is also likely to remain unknowable, must be treated as, for science, non-existent. Hence the sweeping philosophic inferences drawn from Heisenberg's Principle of Uncertainty. Hence also the unwillingness of physicists in general to interest themselves in speculations which, initially, are outside the range of mathematics.

The purpose of this essay is to offer for consideration some speculations, in the province where philosophy and physics meet, which are not supported by mathematical proofs, and which cannot, at the present time, seek or expect such support. It is therefore necessary, in the first instance, to submit reasons in defence of a non-mathematical approach. This involves some inquiry into the relation between nature and mathematics.

3

We must define those terms. I am here using the word Nature to denote the universe apart from man. This is, of course, an arbitrary exclusion. Biologically, men are as much a part of nature as any other organisms. Emerson was logical when he said, "Nature, which made the mason, made the house." Nevertheless, since a great part of our philosophical discussions are concerned with the relations between ourselves, on the one hand, and this globe that we inhabit and the cosmos of which it forms part, on the other, it is convenient to employ some simple, compendious term to express the second factor to the exclusion of the first. This is in fact the ordinary usage of the word Nature.

Everyone would say that a forest, a flock of birds, a river, an eclipse are 'natural'; but not a canal, a town, a machine—anything that is man-made.

I am using the term Mathematics, again in the ordinary sense, to cover any kind of abstract measurement or calculation.

Let me add a brief note on the term Real. I accept from Whitehead that "the event is the unit of things real." An event is any kind of happening—the movement of an electron or of a star in relation to other particles or other astral bodies; a thought in a mind or an action of a body; an occurrence in the life of a man or in the history of a nation—any and every phenomenon may be analysed into events. An event is anything that happens. Yet it is well to remember that you cannot have something happening to nothing. (The grin of the Cheshire cat in *Alice in Wonderland,* which remained some time after the rest of the cat had vanished, is hardly a defensible conception in metaphysics.)

'An object' Whitehead regards as a collection of events which endures. "It is essential," he says, "to grasp the distinction between an object and an event. An object is some entity which we can recognize and meet again; an event passes and is gone."

All events, whether mental or material, form part of reality. Religious beliefs and systems of politics, for example, play a great part in deciding the actions of peoples, and scientific theories in modifying their environment. If the beliefs, systems, and theories had been different, our daily lives would now be in many respects different. But it is confusing to use the word Real, indiscriminately and without qualification, to cover two such different categories as ideas and what we usually describe as 'things.' Language should be fitted to fact: there is a factual distinction between a class that consists of mental concepts, and a class that comprises the stars, the land and the sea, atoms, molecules, and organisms. While accepting both classes as real, it is convenient to distinguish the second class by describing it as 'physically real.'

For example, the poets and myth-makers of ancient Egypt and Greece conceived creatures such as a lion with a woman's head or a horse with a man's head and torso. Egyptian sculptors made rows of stone sphinxes to decorate the approaches to the temples, and Greek artists ornamented vases with figures of centaurs. Those conceptions, as such, are part of the real universe. But no one would contend that thereby sphinxes and centaurs become physical realities.

Or, to take an illustration of a different kind, suppose that Chippendale has an idea for a chair. That idea is real in the sense that it exists in his mind and has involved localized action of some kind in certain of the cells in his brain. It may also be embodied later on in a design that could be used by a furniture-maker as a pattern. If Chippendale had ever existed, and if that idea had not existed, the universe would have been to that extent different. Also the cellular action in the brain is physically real; and so is the design, in so far as it consists of pencil marks on a piece of paper. But neither the mental concept nor the design is physically real as chair, and for the purposes of a chair. If Chippendale were tired he could not sit down on them. Only if and when the craftsman has taken actual pieces of wood, and, with his hands and tools, has shaped and joined them, do we get something which is physically real as chair and can serve the purpose of a chair in relation to other physical realities. In other words, the idea of the chair is one thing; the chair itself is another. Both are real, in the sense that they are parts of the real universe, some aspects of which we perceive. But they are of different orders of reality. Similarly the ideas in a book, which constitute its meaning, are of a different order from the paper, ink-marks, and binding which constitute the book as a material object. And so with all other mental concepts.

4

The point, line, and plane-surface of Euclid are avowedly fictions. To recall his definitions—a point is that which has no parts, or magnitude; a line is length without breadth; a superficies is that which has only length and breadth. These did not purport to have, and cannot have, physical reality. Similarly with arithmetical numbers and algebraical symbols; also diagrams, plans, maps, and statistics. These have reality as paper and ink, but not the same kind of reality as the things that they signify. A surveyor measures a piece of land with a chain, and then makes a plan to a scale; a navigator plots the proposed course of his ship on a chart ruled in lines of longitude and latitude; a doctor measures his patient's symptoms by degrees on a thermometer and by counting his pulse-beats; a merchant in his office has lists of the quantities of goods in his warehouse; a government takes at intervals a census of the people and tabulates their ages, their births, deaths, marriages, and the like, as guides for its policies. In all these cases and innumerable others the figments of mathematics are useful; they are indispensable in practical affairs. And no one for a moment regards the surveyor's map as of the same order as the land; the chart is not confused with the ship's furrow through the sea, the graph of temperatures and pulse-beats with the fever, the stock-lists with the goods, the census with the population. Everyone recognizes as self-evident that nature is one thing and mathematical measurements are another. But at present that is not always so in physics. The distinction between fictional abstractions and physical facts is no longer clear cut; it is becoming blurred.

A widely-used text-book, Richtmyer and Kennard's *Introduction to Modern Physics,* speaks of "a general tendency, notable during the last half-century but regretted by many, for the fundamentals of physics to become an abstract mathematical theory unsupported by underlying concrete ideas." Further, "It seems as if theoretical physics were coming to be based upon certain mathematical assumptions rather than upon concrete pictures of reality." To quote again A. N. Whitehead—eminent as mathematician as well as philosopher—"Mathematics is now being transformed into the intellectual analysis of types of pattern. . . . The essential characterization of mathematics is the study of pattern in abstraction from the particulars which are patterned." He speaks also "of confining thought to purely formal relations which then masquerade as reality. . . . Science relapses into the study of differential equations. The concrete world has slipped through the meshes of the scientific net." He concludes: "There can be no true physical science which looks first to mathematics for the provision of a conceptual model. Such a procedure is to repeat the errors of the logicians of the middle ages."

5

One example of this tendency has a close bearing upon the proposition which will be put forward in the latter part of this essay. We must consider it before we go further. It is the principle, now generally accepted by physicists, which forms part of Einstein's Theory of Relativity, that the medium for the propagation of electromagnetic radiation, of gravity, and of motion in general is a Spacetime Continuum.

Einstein showed conclusively that, if we accept space and time as given factors in the universe, the two cannot be separated from one another. There cannot be a place at no time, or a time nowhere. I may say, for instance, that I am going to Scotland next Tuesday; but I cannot go to Scotland—there *is* no Scotland—apart from some day or other, nor can there be a day unlocated. To be strictly accurate I should have said that I was going to 'Scotland-as-it-will-be-on-Tuesday.' It follows that the three spatial dimensions are always combined with the one temporal dimension, so forming a four-dimensional continuum. Einstein also showed that it is not possible to establish any absolute space, or time, or motion, in the universe as a whole, but that all must be relative to some particular frame of reference. On this basis he proceeded to assume properties in spacetime, such as 'curvature,' 'distortions,' 'hills and declensions,' which would account for actual phenomena in the real universe. He employed mathematical methods that succeeded in revealing phenomena in nature which had not previously been discovered. The spacetime continuum was then accepted by physicists as the medium by which radiation, gravity, and motion in general are propagated. All the phenomena that we see around us were to be described in terms of the 'metrical properties' of spacetime.

But the whole of this system, as an explanation of the working of the actual universe, involves the assumption that space and time themselves are physically real. If not, whether separate or combined, they could have no contact with the system of nature. The two systems would be asymptotic to one another. They might exactly correspond; the one might truthfully portray the other; but they could never touch; they could never cross the gulf that there is between figment and fact. It is as impossible for a mental concept directly to affect a physical process as it would be for a zoo to include in its collection a centaur and a sphinx.

The issue, then, entirely depends upon the answer that we give to the question whether space and time are physically real.

They form so integral a part of all our thinking, and are so essential a framework for our practical life, that commonsense has always taken it for granted that they are, and science and philosophy have usually done the same. Nevertheless some philosophers in the past, and many more nowadays, have not accepted this assumption as valid. They hold, on the contrary, that Space and Time are nothing more than the names which language gives to the patterns of relationship between objects and events among themselves, these being the only physical realities. Quoting Whitehead once more, "Space and time have their origin in the relations between events" (and objects are collections of events).

Objects and events occur, not all-together, but extended, some here, some there: we say that they occur 'in' space. They do not occur all-at-once, but as a succession, some were then, some are now: we say they occur 'in' time. By using those expressions, we have, perhaps unconsciously, implied that there must exist a space and a time for the objects and events to be 'in'; and that these must be of the same order of reality as themselves—otherwise the objects and events could not be contained by the space and time.

But, these philosophers say, that is ill-founded. Space and time are not physical facts but man-made figments. They are of the same order as Euclidean points, lines and planes, numbers, longitude and latitude, and the rest. Space, not being physically real, cannot, by any 'curvatures' or the like, affect in any way the behavior of things which are physically real; it cannot, for example, sustain a beam of light in its passage from a lamp to an object, or lift the water of the sea in tides, or give 'momentum' to a ball thrown from the hand. Indeed to speak of 'the metrical properties of spacetime' is a tautology. For spacetime is *nothing but* metrical. One might as well speak of the enumerating properties of numbers.

The conception of a spacetime continuum has yielded

results of the greatest value to the physicist, results that are correct and reliable within their sphere; just as trigonometry has served the surveyor, logarithms the navigator, arithmetic the merchant, algebra the engineer. All these instruments of the mind may be made to follow exactly the patterns of the real universe. Through them we can deal mentally, in speech and in writing, with the factual phenomena around us, and not be limited to our eyes, ears and hands, our telescopes, microscopes, or balances; and often we can deal with them better. But these proceedings still belong to the realm of mathematics, not of nature. They may lead indirectly to human action which may influence the processes of nature—through the applications of physics, chemistry, and other sciences in practical affairs. But they cannot themselves directly influence natural processes.

Invaluable as the main propositions of Relativity Theory have been, it seems that this one must be excepted. The spacetime continuum has every qualification to enable it to account for the physical phenomena of the universe and only one disqualification—that it does not exist.

6

A second initial objection may be raised to the propositions to be offered in this essay. Not only are they at this stage non-mathematical; they also deal largely with non-observables. But present-day physics holds that precise observation is the only road to scientific truth. Therefore such propositions would be inadmissible.

Professor Max Born, in a work recently published,

says of Reality that he "cannot see any other reasonable interpretation of this word in physics than that it should be understood to mean the sum of observational invariants" —these he has previously defined as "permanent features of observation."

Sir Richard Gregory has lately written that Science is now commonly understood to mean "organized and formulated knowledge of natural objects and phenomena derived from verifiable observations and experiments."

Richtmyer and Kennard say, in the text-book already referred to: "Since 1900 it has become increasingly accepted as a principle of physics that only magnitudes which can be observed, directly or indirectly, have physical significance."

Such quotations might be multiplied. Indeed they express a principle which scientists generally would not only accept, but would regard as unquestionable. Nevertheless, from the philosophic side, it may be questioned.

Inference from what has been observed may, in very many cases, give us valid indications of the existence, character, and behavior of unobservables. The scientist is thinking all the time of ascertainments and measurements of events; the philosopher is trying to keep his eye on the events themselves. The discoveries of science ensue from the existence of phenomena: the existence of phenomena is not conditioned in any way by the discoveries of science. In other words, reality is not dependent on observation.

Things existed in themselves—atoms and molecules, gases, liquids and solids, stars and plents—aeons before man existed. The processes of nature went on for uncounted ages before man came to perceive, observe, and measure them: we have every reason to believe that they go on still, regardless of the presence or absence of human appreciation. No theory of physics—or metaphysics either —can hold good which would not be valid for the universe before man; or for the universe now, beyond the narrow limits of his vision.

In spite of definitions such as I have quoted, science has indeed always recognized this very obvious fact, and does so now. Sir Arthur Eddington was continually emphasizing this. He wrote, for example: "For the reader resolved to eschew theory and admit only definite observational facts, all astronomical books are banned. There are no purely observational facts about the heavenly bodies. Astronomical measurements are, without exception, measurements of phenomena occurring in a terrestrial observatory or station; it is only by theory that they are translated into knowledge of a universe outside." They are translated through inference.

Inference, no doubt, is less reliable than observation. Either indeed may mislead—witness our direct observation, as men thought, of the sun and all the heavens revolving daily round the earth. That is reason for caution, and for the greater caution in cases of inference; but it is not a reason for holding that its results are necessarily worthless.

Sir Edmund Whittaker, in a recent work of great interest, *From Euclid to Eddington,* has this passage:

"By way of preface to this inquiry, we may remark that the world of physics may be divided into (1) *phenomena,* namely, observations, or statements which may be inferred from observations in a direct and simple way; and (2) what Professor Reichenbach calls *interphenomena,* namely the unobservable events which happen between the phenomena. For example, the adventures of light between its emission and its impact on matter belong to the class of interphenomena: so does the process by which an electron in an atom is transferred from one orbit to another when the atom makes a transition between two stationary states. In this category must also be included all hidden structures which are postulated in order to account for observable effects, and, in particular, all localizations of potential energy." We must examine this somewhat closely because much depends in the argument upon whether this view is accepted or not.

We are told in the definition that the interphenomena are "events which happen." We know indeed that they must happen because, if not, the effects which we have actually observed could not be accounted for. Why then should events which are real—since they happen—be excluded from the ordinary category of phenomena and reduced to a lower status?

If this is merely a verbal point, arising from the original meaning of the Greek word, *Phainomenon,* translated as 'appearance,' then there may be some reason for making the distinction. What we observe has 'appeared' to us; what we infer has not. But to change, on this ground, the ordinary usage of the word would be to cause a great deal of inconvenience, for a purpose that would be merely pedantic. For centuries the term Natural Phenomena has been understood to include all the occurrences of nature; to limit it henceforth to those which are observed or observable would require every reader of a book of science or philosophy to bear in mind, from now on, a difference in its connotation. This would be more likely to confuse than the more precise etymology would clarify.

But if the point is not verbal—and Sir Edmund Whittaker does not so present it—then, we would submit with respect, it cannot be accepted as valid. For it implies that the fact of non-observability has some objective consequence: it removes certain events from the ordinary class of phenomena, and it implies for them a different nature, requiring a special name.

Such a distinction, however, is purely subjective, relating only to the human appreciation of one kind of event as against another. There cannot be degrees of reality among physical events and objects. Either they occur and exist, or they do not. If they do, they are real and are phenomena; if not, not. In other words, an event that happens is, by virtue of that fact, a phenomenon: if it is not a phenomenon, then we must have been mistaken in thinking that it had happened.

There are degrees, but they are in the value of our knowledge. We may for a time think that a particular belief is true, when in fact it is false, as with dream-events and hallucinations. Or we may regard it as possible—or probable—or almost certain—or finally as having been established as fact. But these purely subjective distinctions must not be carried across and treated as though they belonged to the object. The object is not concerned with what we may think about it, or whether we think about it at all. A fallacy is involved in the idea of 'inter-phenomena'; it arises from a failure to distinguish between nature itself and our own perceptions and descriptions of nature, between the total of what nature has to show and the part that we are able to see.

Or the matter may be put in another way. The process of induction proceeds from individual observed facts to general principles. The difference of opinion arises on the question whether the process of deduction takes us back only to the same classes of observables, or whether it may also include, by inference, related non-observables. Mathematical physicists are taking the first view; many philosophers take the other.

We reach, then, this conclusion with regard to non-observables. We can say, if we wish, that our knowledge of their existence depends only on inference, and that a particular inference is doubtful. Or we may sometimes be in a position to say that the grounds of the inference are so strong that we should be justified in acting upon it, unless and until fresh reasons are adduced for thinking it wrong. But we are not bound to concur, with Professor Born and others, in a general principle that there is no reality outside the limits of observational invariants; or with Professor Whittaker, that facts (events that happen) revealed by inference are any less the phenomena of nature (in the usual sense of the term) than those revealed by observation. While no doubt it would be wrong to assert as scientifically proved the existence of any object or process that is unobservable, it is also wrong to assert the non-existence of all unobservables—"what I don't know isn't knowledge."

Bertrand Russell said not long ago, "I think myself that the principle of rejecting unobservables, while ad-

explosion of gas in his house; the evidence showed that there had been a gas leakage one night in the basement, and that he had gone to look for it with a lighted candle. Accordingly the Coroner's Court has returned a verdict that that had been the cause of the death, by misadventure. For legal and any other practical purposes that would be sufficient. But if we were to analyse the matter more closely we should find that although the death was due to the explosion and the explosion to the man's own action, both the explosion and the action were the consequences of a whole concatenation of previous events. For instance, the man did not know, or had forgotten, that it is dangerous to look for a gas leak with a naked light; he happened to have at hand a candle and not an electric torch; a leak had occurred owing to faulty plumbing, or to a tap not having been properly turned off; his house was lighted by gas and not by electricity;—and more remotely, the domestic use of a gas liable to explode had been introduced in the nineteenth century; coal measures existed geologically; also that this man had been born, and was alive at that time and present at that spot. Few of these circumstances were relevant for the purposes of the Coroner's Court, and it would have been absurd to have taken them into account; yet all of them came into the causal complex, because, if any one of them had been absent, that explosion would not have happened and that man would not have been killed.

Exactly the same reasoning as applies in a case such as this applies to any and every event—trivial or important, past, present, or future—in human experience or in the course of nature. Each event has its individual character because it is consequent upon a combination of prior events, which has also been individual. The same kind of combination may be repeated again and again, with the same kind of consequence: it becomes a pattern. Nevertheless each event in its turn is unique, having followed upon a combination of events, which may have belonged to a type, but which was, itself, unique.

[Let it be added parenthetically—for this is outside the scope of the present essay but is necessary in order to avoid misunderstanding—that a determinism of this sort does not conflict with the doctrine of human freewill. In the combination of events, which is the cause of any particular event within the sphere of human activity, there will always be a number of actions by persons, following upon individual decisions of their own. Indeed the causes might conveniently be classified as natural, social, and personal all interacting with each other. In the illustration of the gas explosion, the decision of the man himself to go and look for the leak with a candle was his own free choice; also the action or inaction of whoever had been responsible for the faulty plumbing or for leaving the tap not properly turned off. These decisions were autonomous; those people might have chosen to do otherwise; other people in their places would usually have done otherwise. The action of each of them was the result of his character and habits; and those in turn were the result of earlier causes, prenatal and postnatal, internal and external. But that opens up further questions which cannot be discussed here. The immediate point is that free decisions of individual persons form part, and usually a decisive part, in the causation of human events. The position here taken is, therefore, neither materialistic nor fatalistic. It recognizes freewill, but as inside and not outside the vast complex of causality.]

If theoretical physicists are often shy of the word Caused, they are repelled by the word Explain. When we ask for an explanation of Momentum, or Gravitation, or whatever it may be, they demur at once. They say—What do you mean by Explanation? You can describe, mathematically or otherwise, an object, or a phenomenon, or relations between a number of objects or of phenomena, but you can never *explain* anything. At best you can only substitute a further problem for the one you are examining.

Yet a defence can be offered for the word Explanation, and the idea it signifies. It is in fact a useful and quite legitimate word; it is easily understood; and, if we consider the discoveries of science to have been worth while, it is well to remember that all of them have originated in the search for explanations.

Men noticed, for example, ages ago that occasionally the sun or the moon would turn dark for a short time. They asked why these darkenings should occur. Some thought that they were the work of an evil spirit: among the Chinese, so it is said, that it was a vast invisible dragon that was swallowing the sun or the moon—although fortunately it could be driven away again by beating gongs and firing crackers. Some thought that eclipses were portents, arranged by the gods as warnings to particular groups of human beings against some enterprise that they had in hand, or of the impending death of a person of importance.[2] Afterwards, for long periods, it was generally accepted as unnecessary, and also impious, to seek any explanation; except that God, who had made the universe, intervened in each case to cause the eclipse by his own volition and for his own reasons.

Then records began to be kept, and it was discovered that the eclipses occurred at fixed intervals, showing that they were not random events, but were governed by physical laws. Finally it was found that they could be completely accounted for by attributing to the earth and the moon certain movements in relation to one another and in relation to the sun: whenever those movements brought the earth in a direct line between the sun and the moon, the moon was darkened; whenever they brought the moon between the sun and the earth, the sun was darkened. Calendars could be drawn up which stated in advance the day and the hour when the eclipses would take place; invariably, when the time arrived, it was found that they did so. It is true that the discovery of the movement of the astral bodies still left the further problem why there should be such motions; but at all events it was made certain that the explanations of the eclipses that had previously been given, with their evil spirits, portents, dragons, gongs, and crackers, or their specific

[2] Professor Arnold Toynbee quotes Virgil's lines attributing an eclipse to the sun having "veiled his countenance" because of the sins of the Romans which had reached their climax in the assassination of Julius Caesar. "This traditional association," he says, "of an eclipse of the sun with the death of a hero who is being cut off in his prime by a heinous piece of foul play can be traced back to the legend of Herakles."

acts of God on each occasion, were false explanations, while that which gave the movements of the astral bodies as the cause was true.

As to the further problem, for more than fifteen hundred years, from the time of Hipparchus and Ptolemy to the time of Copernicus and Kepler, elaborate systems of astronomy were accepted which explained the movement of the various kinds of astral bodies by imagining the existence of a series of invisible crystalline spheres. These spheres revolved about the earth as their common center, at different distances and with different velocities, carrying around the moon, sun, planets, and stars. Dante supposed that the movement of each of these spheres was caused by individual Intelligences or Spirits, assigned to that duty. Here again others thought it enough to say that the motion was the work of God—either set going once for all or continuously sustained. Then Newton showed that the motion was governed by gravitation, which operated according to the inverse-square law; but the motion itself he did not seek to explain. Whitehead takes the same position. Einstein attributes the motion of the astral bodies to "the metrical properties of space," but no answer that is generally acceptable, is given to the objection that Space itself is no more than a mental concept, and therefore can perform no physical functions in the real universe of observed phenomena. So we reach the situation in which we find ourselves at this moment. All the explanations offered having failed to satisfy, the main trend among theoretical physicists is to give up trying; and to justify the surrender by asserting that explanation is never possible of anything. Yet—among many examples —eclipses were explained quite satisfactorily; and, in other provinces of science, chemical combinations have been explained, up to a certain point, by the discovery of atoms and their interrelations; and the origin of species by the principle of evolution, natural selection, and Mendelian genetics. Nor is there any reason in the nature of things why we should suppose that stellar motion, and impetus in general, or gravitation, or radiation, can never be accounted for to an equal degree—their *causes* discovered and the phenomena *explained.* "Under every deep a lower deep opens," says Emerson. To have succeeded in sounding one encourages us to attempt the next.

8

As to the question of Cause and Chance—to which we now return—that issue has become prominent in our time because of the promulgation of Heisenberg's Principle of Indeterminacy—afterwards renamed the Uncertainty Principle—and the deductions as to causality that have been drawn from it. During twenty years of controversy it has become apparent that most, though not all physicists have accepted those deductions, while many, probably most, philosophers have not.

As long ago as 1931 Einstein had dissented. In a letter sent to me for publication he wrote: "I mentioned to you in conversation that I, too, was unable to regard as final the present tendency of theoretical physicists to reject the postulate of causality or determinism. . . . They maintain that a deterministic theory is to be rejected, and that it is merely conservatism based on custom and prejudice to search after such a theory. In this they go, in my opinion, too far." Some years later, in the course of a published conversation, Einstein said: "Indeterminism is quite an illogical concept. . . . If I say that the average life-span of such an atom is indetermined in the sense of being not caused, then I am talking nonsense." And Professor Born quotes, in the book to which I have referred, letters from Einstein written in 1944 and 1947 in which he says, "You believe in the dice-playing god, and I in the perfect rule of law in a world of something objectively existing which I try to catch in a wildly speculative way. . . . I see of course that the statistical interpretation . . . has a considerable content of truth. Yet I cannot seriously believe it because the theory is inconsistent with the principle that physics has to represent a reality in space and time without phantom action over distances. . . . I am absolutely convinced that one will eventually arrive at a theory in which the objects connected by laws are not probabilities, but conceived facts, as one took for granted only a short time ago."

Planck wrote in the same sense and with equal emphasis: "To-day there are eminent physicists who under the compulsion of facts are inclined to sacrifice the principle of strict causality in the physical view of the world. . . . So far as I can see, however, there is no ground for such a renunciation." Elsewhere he puts the question: "Does scientific practice intimate that there are certain happenings in nature where the law of causation does not function, and that there are regions in the mental sphere where the causal writ does not run?" And he gives the answer: "Physical science (*i.e.*, physics), together with astronomy and chemistry and mineralogy are all based on the strict and universal validity of the principle of causality. In a word, this is the answer which physical science has to give to the question asked." Since it is contended that indeterminism is a necessary consequence of Quantum Mechanics, it is interesting to note that Planck, the originator of the Quantum Theory, has written: "One cannot yet definitely say what influence the subsequent development of the hypothesis may have on the formulation of fundamental physical laws. Some essential modification seems to be inevitable; but I firmly believe, in company with most physicists, that the quantum hypothesis will eventually find its exact expression in certain equations which will be a more exact formulation of the law of causality."

The conclusion is that we may accept from the physicists that there are certain phenomena which cannot be 'determined' in the sense of ascertained or measured, by the technique of science; but that we need not agree that it follows that those phenomena are not 'determined' in the sense of caused, in accordance with the laws of nature. Bertrand Russell stated the case from the philosophic standpoint simply and tersely when he said, "In one sense of the word a quantity is determined when it is measured, in the other sense an event is determined when it is caused. The Principle of Indeterminacy has to do with measurement, not with causation."

9

Let us consider now a little further the conception of Chance and whether, if there were need for some supplement to causality, this could provide it.

The word Chance has always been in common use to denote whatever happens fortuitously, without known cause; we therefore accept Chance unquestioningly, as being a real agency acting in the universe. Professor Born, writing on the natural philosophy of Cause and Chance, does not start with any definition of the word, or stay to examine whether it denotes anything that is factual, in the sense that the events which it is supposed to govern are factual. Apparently he considers that common usage is sufficient. But when we come to investigate the matter more closely we shall find that it is far from sufficient.

Let us take one or two examples. Go to the very temple of Chance, a gambling casino, and look at the roulette table. A horizontal wheel, divided into numbered compartments, is set revolving by the croupier, and he launches a ball into it in the opposite direction; when the wheel comes to rest and the ball drops into one of the compartments, that number wins. The results are, for us, pure chance, in the sense that there is no possibility of our predicting them. Yet, as a matter of fact, the difference of the result in each case depends upon two factors that are strictly causal—the velocity of the wheel when it is set revolving and the velocity of the ball when it is thrown in. And each of these depends upon the degree of effort on the part of the croupier in moving his arm. It would be possible to devise a machine which would start the roulette revolving and throw in the ball; and if the machine were nicely adjusted, and all interference by air-currents or otherwise excluded, the same number could be made to win every time.[3] But the croupier's arm not being a machine, neither he nor anyone else can gauge the amount of force that is being exerted on any particular occasion. Once the movements of the arm have been made, the result will follow with certainty. The causes are there. The element we term Chance consists merely in the impossibility of our ascertaining and measuring those causes.

Or we might hear in the railway carriage, going up to town in the morning, someone say this: "My elderly neighbor had a most unfortunate accident yesterday. He happened not to put on his spectacles, and when he went out did not see a piece of orange-peel which chanced to be on the path just outside his gate: he slipped and broke his leg. It was sheer bad luck, the sort of accident that might happen to anyone." But if we were to re-state the incident omitting the tendentious words 'unfortunate . . . accident . . . happened . . . chanced . . . bad luck,' we might reach a different conclusion. Two sets of prior events were involved: someone walking along the footway eating an orange had dropped a piece of peel just outside that gate, and a short-sighted man living in the

[3] A machine has in fact been made, for use in cricket practice, which will deliver a ball again and again uniformly; speed, pitch, and break are changeable and regulated beforehand. Photographs of the machine were given in *The Illustrated London News*, of October 22, 1949.

house had forgotten to put on his glasses before going out. From the combination of those two sets of causes the result followed. It could have been foreseen. In fact someone might well make the comment that, if careless people drop orange-peel on the pavement and short-sighted people neglect to put on their spectacles, injuries are bound to occur sooner or later.

Considered subjectively, as from the individual concerned, all such events may be regarded as the result of 'luck,' of pure chance. Considered mathematically, the chances of their occurring can be calculated, according to the rules of probability, on the basis of past experience. Considered in themselves, as part of the operations of the universe, each event is unique, the consequence of a particular combination of prior events which has occurred in that place, at that moment, once for all.

10

Mr. John Buchan (Lord Tweedsmuir) dealt with the question of chance, not in connection with physics, nor yet with ordinary experiences of daily life, but with events in history. Giving the Rede Lecture in Cambridge in 1929 he took as his subject *The Causal and the Casual in History.* His purpose was to make us "recognize the fundamental irrationality of a large part of Clio's domain." He says, "Rationalize the facts as much as you please—and you can often carry the process a long way—there will remain things which you cannot rationalize, things which you can only call accidents, and which cannot be explained by any logical terms. Instead of the causal we find the casual. I do not for one moment argue that these incomprehensible factors are incapable of rationalization by some higher intelligence than our own; I only say that we cannot fit them into any mortal scheme of effects and causes." He adds: "An historical event can be partially explained by many causes, but there may be some little thing without which it could not have happened, and that little thing may come out of the void, without any apparent justification for its existence. Nevertheless, but for it the history of a decade or a century would have gone differently."

Buchan gives several interesting examples to illustrate his theme. The eldest son of King James I happened to catch an infection from which he died at the age of 18; had he lived, a man with the abilities and opinions of which he had already shown signs, he would have adopted policies very different from those of his brother Charles, who succeeded to the throne. If the Prince had not chanced to catch the infection, there would probably, Buchan says, have been no Civil War.

Again, during the Jacobite Rebellion in 1745 there was a moment when, if the army of Prince Charles had pressed on, it would very likely have taken London; the Stuarts would have been restored to the throne and the whole course of events, then and later, would have been changed. It depended upon the way the balance of debate inclined at a certain council of leaders held in Derby one night in December: and the opportunity was missed.

A more recent instance quoted was the death of King Alexander of Greece in 1920 from blood-poisoning—due to the bite of a pet monkey. That was followed by dynastic and diplomatic changes, which resulted in the rout of the Greek armies by the Turks and the catastrophes that followed. Mr. Churchill said, "A quarter of a million persons died of that monkey's bite."

Buchan's charm of style lends plausibility to his thesis, but it cannot carry conviction as to its truth. For of course we cannot seriously attempt to divide all the events of human history into two categories, one causal, the other casual. Indeed Buchan himself says, "To look for such pregnant trifles is an instructive game, very suitable for academic circles in the winter season"; and he introduces his examples by saying, "Let me offer to you—in the spirit of the game which I have suggested—one or two cases where destiny does seem for one moment to have trembled in the balance."

The fact is that among the antecedents of important events in history have often been some incidents which, at the time they happened, appeared to be trivial or insignificant. No one could then have foreseen that, in conjunction with others, they would share in bringing about events that were momentous. But that does not take them out of the causal complex and place them in a separate category—the casual or accidental. We must not invent some little metaphysical demon, called Chance, to be responsible for whatever cannot be explained otherwise; able to produce "incomprehensible factors out of the void," as Buchan says, which, according to Professor Born, "certain events obey." Here again the dichotomy is between what is ascertained or ascertainable and what is not. The division is not between caused and uncaused. The lacuna is in our own knowledge, not in nature's processes. As

Leslie Stephen said, "Chance is a name for our ignorance."

The phrase "the laws of chance" is self-contradictory. If it is chance, then there are no laws: if there are laws, then it is not chance.

11

Statistics is a science and, like every other science, has its own laws governing its own methods and procedures. But these are internal; and when it is said that there are also 'statistical laws' of a different kind, with some jurisdiction in the external world, and that by them "causality is satisfactorily explained," it may be well to pause and consider before we assent.

Statistics follow and tabulate one set of events, and precede and may predict another set of similar events. But they do not cause or determine the second set of events. They have no effect that is in any way equivalent to causality.

The life-tables of an insurance company will tell, with approximate accuracy, how many people in each age-group will die next year in this country. But no one thinks for a moment that the life-tables have anything to do with the actual occurring of the deaths. Each individual dies from his own special cause—some malady or disease, or old age, or perhaps an accident or a crime. He does not die, "in obedience to statistical laws," because he is one of an age-group with a certain life-expectation. This reasoning applies universally; what is true in such a case as this is equally true in every other, particles and atoms not excepted.

An example often offered by those who hold a different view is the disintegration of the radium atom. It is found, by calculation based on observation, that, in any quantity of radium, in the period of a year one atom in 1700 will explode. Scientific technique enables this to be said with some assurance; but which particular atom in the 1700 it will be, it cannot ever attempt to determine. Therefore, it is said, the choice is purely fortuitous. "Fate knocks at the door" of one particular atom, and no one can tell which: in that region pure hazard reigns; causality no longer holds; we can get a result only by aggregating the fates of large numbers of atoms and calculating probabilities: thus we reach the ratio of 1 to 1700.

This reasoning is based upon the fact that research can never ascertain the conditions that affect the behavior of any individual atom—its structure, its surrounding field, and the forces, within and without, that are acting upon it. We are therefore obliged to act—if we are to deal with the matter at all—*as if* all the atoms, and their conditions, were exactly alike. But there is no reason why we should believe that assumption to be true; except that if it were not true, the methods we have at our disposal would not suffice to enable us to get any further; and this reason is hardly adequate. On the contrary, the probabilities are that there is some system of causes, unknown to us but uniformly acting, which varies the conditions as between one atom and another. If not, why should there be this regularity, giving a steady average of 1 in 1700? Why not 500 one year and 5 the next, then 50 and then none? It is precisely the presence of causation, and not 'chance,' which enables us to make the statistical prediction. The statistics follow upon the individual events: the events are in no way dependent upon the statistics.

Max Planck realized this clearly and stated it definitely. He says (dealing as an example with molecular heat conduction): "In the point of fact, statistical laws are dependent upon the assumption of the strict law of causality functioning in each particular case. And the nonfulfilment of the statistical rule in particular cases is not therefore due to the fact that the law of causality is not fulfilled, but rather to the fact that our observations are not sufficiently delicate and accurate to put the law of causality to a direct test in each case. If it were possible for us to follow the movement of each individual molecule in this very intricate labyrinth of processes, then we should find in each case an exact fulfilment of the dynamical laws."

The general conclusion is that statistics are consequential and not causal. They are not entitled to any place in the philosophic discussion of the principle of causality. When we have passed beyond the range of observation we can rely upon inference from what has already been observed. Concepts such as statistical laws, probability, chance, like space and time, and systems of geometry—the whole mathematical apparatus, all these are fictional abstractions. They can help to create formative ideas in men's minds, and these may produce concrete results; but they have no dynamic quality in themselves. They cannot *do* anything in the real world. Physically they do not exist, and it is useless trying to set the non-existent to catch the unobservable.

II. Problems Outstanding

1

Philosophers try to keep their eye on the processes of nature themselves and will not be content with their inter-measurements. For the most part they will not agree with Professor Niels Bohr when he speaks of "the old truth that in our description of nature the purpose is not to disclose the real essence of the phenomena but only to track down, as far as possible, relations between the manifold aspects of our experience." They persist in seeking the 'real essence,' through a search for causes; convinced that the nearer we can draw to their causation, whether it lies within our experience or is outside it, the nearer we may approach to what must remain our ultimate goal, the essential nature of the phenomena themselves. Indeed it is to the realm beyond the range of scientific observation and calculation that we may now be well advised to devote our special attention. The other has been so long and so actively explored that it is in this realm, if at all, that solutions to the fundamental problems that are still outstanding are most likely to be found.

Newton is often cited in support of the school which prefers to establish measurements than try to ascertain causes. *Hypotheses non fingo,* he said. But that was an expression of Newton's personal choice of the field for his own activities. He himself preferred to specialize on empirical research and the mathematical investigation of the results; but he was far from suggesting that as a limitation for science in general. Let us remember this passage in the *Opticks,* and particularly its concluding words: "To derive two or three general Principles of Motion from Phaenomena, and afterwards to tell us how the Properties and Actions of all corporeal things follow from those manifest Principles, would be a very great step in Philosophy, though the Causes of those Principles were not yet discover'd: And therefore I scruple not to propose the Principles of Motion above-mention'd, they being of very general Extent, and leave their Causes to be found out."

Our first conclusion, then, from what has been said in the previous section is the negative one that we cannot consent to be debarred *a priori* from the pursuit of causes and confined to measurements: still less to accept the doctrine that, where no measurements are possible, we must take it that no causes exist.

Our second conclusion is also negative—that a mental concept can never by itself be the cause of any physical event. Prior events, that were themselves physical, must have entered. To attribute an occurrence to the action of Chance, Statistical laws, Spacetime, or any other fictional abstraction, is scholastic. It is akin to the attribution of 'occult qualities' to objects. Here again we may refer to Newton—in the same passage in the *Opticks:* "The Aristotelians gave the Name of occult Qualities, not to manifest Qualities, but to such Qualities only as they supposed to lie hid in Bodies, and to be the unknown Causes of manifest Effects: Such as would be the Causes of Gravity, and of magnetick and electrick Attractions, and of Fermentations, if we should suppose that these Forces or Actions arose from Qualities unknown to us, and uncapable of being discovered and made manifest. Such occult Qualities put a stop to the Improvement of natural Philosophy, and therefore of late Years have been rejected. To tell us that every Species of Things is endow'd with an occult specifick Quality by which it acts and produces manifest Effects, is to tell us nothing."

Our third conclusion, which follows from the others, is more positive. It is that—in order to strengthen the future prospect, in fundamental matters, of effective progress through the scientific agencies of observation and calculation—we should try, in the first instance, to open for it a new way of approach. This must be through speculation; in other words, through philosophy.

"Philosophy," says Whitehead, "should aim at disclosure beyond existing presuppositions." And Einstein and Infeld, in *The Evolution of Physics,* say, "Fundamental ideas play the most essential role in forming a physical theory. Books on physics are full of complicated mathematical formulae. But thought and ideas, not formulae, are the beginning of every physical theory. The ideas must later take the mathematical form of a quantitative theory, to make possible the comparison with experiment."

2

Before we go further and try to apply these principles there are two preliminary conditions that have to be stated.

The first is that we must exclude any suggestion that involves in any form action at a distance without an intervening medium. If a combination of physical events at one place gives rise to an event at another place, then this cannot be across sheer void. There must be some kind of contiguity. There must be something in between; and this must be as real as the events themselves are real.

Here again we may pray in aid both Newton and Einstein. Newton wrote this of gravitation—but it applies equally to radiation and to motion in general: "That gravity should be innate, inherent, and essential to matter, so that one body may act upon another at a distance through a vacuum, without the mediation of any thing else, by and through which their action and force may be conveyed from one to another, is to me so great an absurdity, that I believe no man, who has in philosophical matters a competent faculty of thinking, can ever fall into it." And Einstein says, in his *Theory of Relativity:* "As a result of the more careful study of electromagnetic phenomena, we have come [in modern physics] to regard action at a distance as a process impossible without the intervention of some intermediary medium." He instances a 'magnetic field,' and adds, "The effects of gravitation also are regarded in an analogous manner." As he wrote to Max Born, "Physics has to represent a reality in space and time without phantom actions over distances."

A text-book on the Theory of Light says, "Direct action at a distance is out of the question. We cannot conceive of energy disappearing at the sun and reappearing at the earth after an interval of eight minutes without having been propagated continuously in the interval through the intervening space."

The second condition is that we must not look for our medium in any kind of gaseous ether, or an elastic solid ether, such as was postulated by nineteenth-century physicists. This is now universally agreed, and it is not necessary to argue the point. It will be enough to mention, in summary form, the objections which, in combination, have been found conclusive.

1. Their ether was first conceived as of a gaseous order, consisting of particles, but far more tenuous than any known gas. But if it is corpuscular, what is supposed to be between the particles? Must there not be yet another medium that connects them? If so, the basic problem remains unchanged.

2. The motion of stellar bodies through any material medium, whether gaseous or an elastic solid, must give rise to friction. However tenuous the ether might be, the friction, over stretches of time, must have an effect in retarding motion. But there can be found in the movement of the planets and the stars no sufficient evidence of such retardation.

3. If the earth is moving through any such ether it ought to be possible, by terrestrial experiment, to measure the velocity of its motion. In 1887, the American scientists, Michelson and Morley, devised a method for attempting this. That the mechanism of the experiment was properly designed for its purpose was not disputed. The test was made, by them and by other physicists, again and again, in several countries, over many years and in a great variety

of conditions. The results were conclusive, and they were overwhelmingly negative—no movement at all could be detected. Since the motion of the earth round the sun must be taken as a fact, and since the most thorough investigation could not relate this movement to an ether of the kind supposed, only one deduction was possible—that no such ether existed.

4. The theory of relativity has added another objection of an equally fundamental character. It has been succinctly stated by Whittaker in his recent book: "Most of the solid [1] and liquid aethers of the nineteenth century had one feature which in the end proved fatal to them, namely, they were constituted of identifiable structural elements whose position could be traced from moment to moment, so that the phrase 'velocity relative to the aether' had a meaning, and consequently they were bound up with the principle that it is possible to define absolute velocity in space. With the advent of the theory of relativity in 1905, this principle was seen to be erroneous, and the search for a quasi-material aether came to an end."

3

Bearing in mind, then, those limitations and conditions, we proceed to consider four of the problems in theoretical physics that will still be outstanding.

1. The first is the nature of electromagnetic radiation and the medium for its transmission. On this a great body of information has been accumulated during the last

[1] 'Solid' in the sense of being a continuum.

two hundred and fifty years, but the basic question remains unanswered.

I turn on a light in my library and sit down to read a book. Or an astronomer in his observatory puts the camera attached to his telescope in the line of a ray of light from a distance galaxy, and the light effect, accumulated during a period of minutes or hours, blackens the molecules of chloride of silver in a photographic plate. What is it that happens, between the lamp and the book and between the book and my eye, that enables me to read? And what has sustained the light from the galaxy during its journey, of perhaps a hundred million years? If we hold that 'space' is a figment, incapable of producing physical effects, present day science gives us no answer.

2. The second problem is similar, but relating to the nature of gravitation and its propagation.

I stand on the seashore and watch the rising tide creeping up the sands under the moon. We say that it is the gravitational pull of the moon on the sea, measured by the mathematical law of the inverse square of the distance, which is raising those millions of tons of water. We know what we mean by 'moon' and we know what we mean by 'sea': they are systems or volumes of immense numbers of molecules, each consisting of atoms of various kinds, each atom with an electronic structure. But what meaning does the mind attach to the words 'gravitational' and 'pull'? What is happening in the moon, between the moon and the sea, and in the sea, to lift the water? It cannot be the mathematical formula that does this. A formula may enable us to measure a force, but it cannot itself do what the force does. What, then, is the gravity which produces results that we see incessant all about us? And how does it operate between a center of attraction and the object attracted?

3. The third problem is the nature of motion in general and the meaning of momentum.

Here it has usually been said that the answer was given, once for all, in Newton's First Law of Motion—"Every body continues in a state of rest, or of uniform motion in a straight line, unless it is compelled to change that state by forces impressed upon it." That, however, is a statement of fact, not an explanation. It sets out clearly what the problem is; it does not solve it. Nor does it purport to do so: Newton did not offer his laws or formulas as anything more than statements of fact.

It is strange that a thinker so precise and critical as Whitehead interprets it differently. In an address recently republished, Whitehead quotes the First Law of Motion with enthusiasm. "This," he says, "is the first article in the creed of science. . . . It should be set to music and chanted in the halls of Universities. It has defeated the heretics, . . . the Aristotelians, who for two thousand years imposed on Dynamics the search for a physical cause of motion. . . . The true doctrine conceives uniform motion in a straight line as a state in which every body will naturally continue except so far as it is compelled by impressed force to change that state."

"Will naturally continue . . .": the word Nature is invoked to provide the clue. To personify the sum of things under the name of Nature is indeed customary in literature, and convenient. But to use the compendious idea of nature as though it could account for a particular physical process, as though it had any potency in itself, is clearly a relapse into scholasticism. It is akin to the medieval cosmogony which held, of the four so-called 'elements,' that it was a 'natural property' of air and fire to go upwards in a straight line, and of earth and water to go down.

Nor does the usual definition of momentum carry us any farther—"the product of the inertial mass of a body and its velocity." We are still left to ask what are the causes of the phenomena or properties that we call inertia, mass, and velocity.

Why should a ball that has been thrown continue, after it has been released from the hand, to travel indefinitely, in a straight line away from the thrower; its direction and velocity modifiable only by the intervention of other forces—the earth's attraction, friction with the air, or the like? Or why should an astral body continue in perpetuity its motion relative to other bodies?

The theory of relativity accounted for anomalies in the motion of the perihelion of Mercury which Newtonian principles could not explain; but it cannot say why Mercury should move in its orbit at all. It predicted correctly that light from a distant star would be found to be deflected when passing near the gravitational mass of the sun, and gave beforehand, almost precisely, the degree of deflection. But it cannot say how those rays of light had been transmitted across astronomical distances. It accepts these as facts that are given: planets circle and light travels because the nature of the universe, and of its space, is such as to make them do so. That is to say, no answer to the question is attempted.

4. The last problem which we cite as still outstanding is the nature of the waves and the particles that are studied by physics and the relations between them. Ever since the days of Newton and Huygens this has given rise to controversies: they seem no nearer solution now. The present situation has been tersely described by Lord Cherwell (Professor F. A. Lindemann): "The current attitude appears to be that electrons, protons, and photons have a corpuscular aspect and an undulatory aspect; that according to the experiment one makes one can observe either the one or the other. This point of view seems a confession of failure rather than an explanation."

In all these matters we appear, for the time being, to be at a dead end.

III. Proposition

1

We look for some clue that might help us to solve all those connected problems simultaneously. For the reasons given, we can only find it, if at all, in something that is physically real. We shall not try to find it through further elaborations of differential equations, nor in the field of logic or of linguistics.

Let us consider first one element in nature, perceptible all around us—active energy.

When we draw a clear-cut line between the physically real and the fictional, energy must be on the real side. If anyone doubts this, let him look at a tree that has been struck by nightning; or let him remember the Japanese cities devastated by the nuclear fission of atoms; or let him think again of the page of a book illuminated by a lamp, or the rising tide. All these are manifestations of pure energy. If they are not that, what are they? When Lord Cherwell writes, "We maintain that energy is just as much a statistical concept as temperature," we can answer that evident facts in our experience, such as those, contradict this contention. It is not a statistical concept that splits the tree or destroys the city, lights the page or lifts the ocean.

Consider, again, some solid material object, accepted

as physically real. The chemist may melt it into a liquid; evaporate the liquid into gas; analyse the gas into molecules and the molecules into atoms. The physicist carries the analysis further, and divides the atom into particles of various kinds. Beyond that he finds energy and nothing else. The atomic engineer confirms him empirically. At what point in that series do we pass from the real to the conceptual, from the material to the mathematical? If there is no such point—and there can be none—then the energy, which constitutes the particles, atoms, molecules of which the object consists, must be as real as the object itself, that reality having been accepted at the outset.

Active energy, therefore, fulfils the first requirement —physical existence in the universe. But that is not enough to give us the clue we are seeking. We ask at once where does this active energy come from? We see its manifestations in heat, light, magnetism, electricity, mechanical work: but we still have no answer to the question, what is the medium which makes possible all such phenomena—action at a distance being excluded. Active energy may be one factor in what we are looking for, but it is not enough by itself. If it had been, our problem would have been solved long ago.

2

The suggestion offered here for consideration—and that is the main purpose of this essay—is a simple one. *It is that energy exists in two states—quiescent and active, and passes easily from one to the other.*

Quiescent energy is conceived as a continuum, and

as the sole physical constituent of the universe. All material events are to be accounted for as cases of the activation of quiescent energy.

Being quiescent it is undifferentiated, and produces no phenomena. It cannot therefore be perceived, or defined, or described, and nothing can be located or timed by reference to it.

It does not follow from this that it is non-existent. Its existence is demonstrated by the emergence and behavior of active energy. It is one of those unobservables whose reality is inferred from the phenomena that have been observed.

If objection is raised to this on the ground that a new unobservable ought not to be admitted, an answer has already been offered in the earlier discussion. But if that answer is also not accepted, then it may be added that the alternative now usually adopted by physicists, a Space-time Continuum, is equally unobservable. Whittaker says on this: "It is true that we do not speak much of the aether nowadays, and certainly do not regard it as a quasi-material medium filling all space; but when we endow space itself (or, in non-statical problems, space-time) with properties such as curvature, we are making it play the part of an aether. The principle that one and the same aether ought to serve for all purposes was enunciated by Faraday himself: 'It is not at all unlikely,' he said, 'that if there be an aether, it should have other uses than simply the conveyance of radiations.'"

The proposition submitted here would not therefore involve an addition to the number of unobservables, which Russell so rightly deprecates where avoidable; but only the substitution of one unobservable for another—and, it is submitted, one that may be more defensible.

While reserving till the concluding sections of this essay a fuller consideration of the conception of quiescent energy, I would mention here two further points:

1. Relativity theory rests in part upon an assumption of 'Inertial systems.' But it is difficult to find, from a study of Einstein's works, to what features in the real universe inertial systems correspond.[1] If quiescent energy were established as a component in the perceived universe it would serve equally as a framework for the inertial systems of relativist mathematics, while not open to the objection of unreality.

2. As long ago as 1900 H. Poincaré adumbrated the principle that *all* energy has the property of inertia. His view has won a large measure of support. But is not this equivalent to saying that *any* energy may *at one time* be inert and *at another time* not inert?—which is the essential principle of the Two-State Ether here proposed.

3

That there should be two material states—or more—of a single entity is familiar to us in nature. Water for example, and many elements and other compounds, may be at one time gaseous, at another time liquid, at another solid. If a copper wire connects a lamp with an electric

[1] See A. Einstein, *The Theory of Relativity*, pp. 65-70; A. Einstein, *The Meaning of Relativity*, pp. 56-59 (Methuen and Co., Ltd., 1946 and 1950); A. Einstein and L. Infeld, *The Evolution of Physics*, pp. 166, 220-225 (Cambridge University Press, 1938).

battery, something in or about the wire is in one state when the current is switched on and in another state when it is off. An elastic substance may be in a relaxed state, then extended, then relaxed again. In the different field of physiology, an animal brain passes from activity to quiescence, or vice versa, in memory or in sleep. Seeds remain inactive indefinitely until the conditions occur that are necessary for germination. If energy is at one place-time quiescent and at another active it would be an instance of one of nature's best known expedients.

Some general term is needed to cover energy in both its forms. Considering the history of this subject, from the time of the Greeks onwards, we can hardly use any other than the word Ether. This involves the danger that we may be supposed still to be thinking of an ether like that conceived by some of the nineteenth-century physicists, and of Newton before them. "Is not this medium," Newton said, "exceedingly more rare and subtile than the air, and exceedingly more elastick and active? And doth it not readily pervade all bodies? And is it not (by its elastick force) expanded through all the Heavens?" The function is indeed the same, and the universality is the same; but it must be emphasized that the constitution of this Ether is fundamentally different. It does not at all resemble air. Its composition is not gaseous or quasi-gaseous, but only energic.

A conception such as this would be in accord with the views of a great physicist of our own day, Sir J. J. Thomson, one of those pioneers whose flashes of genius have lighted up the dark ways of the universe. Towards the end of his life Thomson wrote this to a correspondent: "I differ from you about the value of the conception of an ether, the more I think about it the more I value it. I regard the ether as the working system of the universe. I think all mass momentum and energy are seated there and that its mass momentum and energy are constant, so that Newtonian mechanics apply." This considered opinion of the discoverer of the electron is not to be lightly brushed aside.

IV. Lines of Inquiry

For any who may wish to consider what deductions may be drawn from the principle of a Two-State Ether, possible lines of inquiry are suggested in this section.

Physical phenomena are conceived as originating in transitions from quiescent energy to active and from active to quiescent. Since these processes are the essence of the whole matter, investigation should start with them.

ACTIVATION 1

The nature of quiescent energy being unknown, and probably destined to remain unknown, we cannot attempt to describe activation from its beginning. You cannot describe a physical process within a medium that is itself indescribable. You can only view it backwards, so to speak, from the standpoint of its consequences. We must infer what is likely to have happened from the phenomena which have in fact been produced, and which come, directly or indirectly, within our cognizance.

It would appear that activation may be caused by some kind of impact upon the quiescent ether. But we are assuming that nothing exists other than undifferentiated quiescent ether except active, and therefore differentiated, ether. This, we shall find, so far as at present recognized, is in the form of ether-waves or ether-particles. If there is an impact, it would, therefore, be the impact of waves or particles which had started an activation.

This, however, would not explain the origin of the whole process. For if activation results from the presence of something already in action, what can have happened to cause the first activation of all? This seems to be of the same order as the root problem of biology: so far as has at present been ascertained, it appears that life comes into existence only by growth from something that is already living. But these questions carry us back to the ultimate problem of philosophy: how is it that anything exists at all—energy, matter, mind, ideas, life, God?

On this neither science, nor philosophy, nor yet religion is able to tell us anything. Religion says, "In the beginning God created the heaven and the earth": but that sentence contradicts itself: it could not have been the beginning for God was already there. The philosopher, it has been said, may explain everything—except himself. And as for science, this province lies outside its self-imposed boundaries.

We must start therefore with the conception that, in the actual universe, activation is initiated at particular times and in particular places, possibly by some kind of impact. This would consist of impulses from ether-waves or ether-particles; or groups of particles organized into atoms, or groups of atoms organized into molecules and material objects.

2

In this highly speculative region little can be said with any degree of confidence. It seems probable however that, if there is any activation at all, it must have a starting-point, a specific minimum below which an impact would be ineffective. Unless there were such a 'threshold' the distinction between the two states of quiescence and activity could not be maintained and an ordered universe could not have come into being.

The question presents itself whether this has any relevance to Planck's constant. I venture again to have recourse to Whittaker for a concise description: "Planck assumed that the energy of the minute oscillators, which effectively constitute a radiating substance, exists in discrete bundles of amount $\epsilon = h\nu$, where ν is the frequency and h is the constant occurring above, and that the oscillators can emit or absorb only multiples of $h\nu$. This assumption was the starting-point of the quantum theory. The value of h, which is a universal constant of nature and is called *Planck's constant of Action,* is $6.625 \times [10^{-23}]$ erg. sec."

Since h is indivisible it must be the minimum of something; what is not divisible into fractions is, by that fact, established as a minimum. It seems to be possible that Planck's constant is the measure, in terms of our human standards of measurement, of the least impact that will turn quiescent energy into active. It is a specific point at which one state of an entity changes into another —like a freezing-point or boiling-point.

If applied to an ether system, the description of Planck's constant given above would need to be differently worded. It would no longer be a case of oscillators being able to emit or absorb only multiples of $h\nu$. We shall be supposing that it is the medium which determines the manner of transmission. The ether cannot be activated by impacts of less than one unit of $h\nu$, and it can transmit only in integral units. It is also subject to a specific maximum of velocity, which is dependent upon its own character.

3

A second conjecture is that activation must be a time-process. We know that electromagnetic radiation is not propagated instantaneously throughout the universe, but is consecutive. It is transmitted at a specific velocity, measurable in miles per second, and needs vast periods of time to travel from one region of the universe to another. If activation is to be conceived as a general system of which radiation is one example, then we may suppose, unless reason is given to the contrary, that activation is itself a time-process.

Incidentally, this temporal nature of radiation may be cited in support of the view that it has to do with a medium which is material and not mathematical. It is also to be expected that radiation–and activation in general–should be subject to other mechanical laws such as are known to prevail elsewhere in nature.

WAVES 1

Proceeding on the assumption of an activated ether, we gain an idea of its patterns from the result of the intensive study of radiation and of electronics during the last fifty or sixty years. It may take the form sometimes of a series of waves, sometimes of individual coherent particles.

It is now generally accepted as probable that radiation is emitted by oscillators, the wave-form being a consequence of the oscillation. An example often given is that of a length of flexible cord held suspended in the hand: if the hand is moved horizontally to and fro, a succession of waves travels perpendicularly down the cord to the free end. This illustration, however, is liable to mislead, because radiation is emitted, not in lines, but in expanding spheres.

(I am dealing here with perceptible radiation from an aggregation of atoms and not with the light emitted from a single atom, which, as Einstein has shown, has different characteristics.)

When a candle is lighted in a room the light is propagated in every direction equally: walls, floor and ceiling are all illuminated. The statement, made from the time of the Greeks and still sometimes heard, that light is emitted in straight lines is mistaken. Nature knows nothing of rectilinear rays—with one exception—unless they occur accidentally: for example when a portion of a train of spherical waves of sunlight is obstructed by clouds, or perhaps by the foliage of a forest, and, through interstices in the clouds or in the foliage, we see the sun's radiance shining in straight lines. The one exception is the animal eye, which has a bi-convex lens as part of its mechanism: this collects a pencil out of any train of spherical waves impinging on the eye and conveys it in straight lines to the retina. We are thereby misled into thinking that what we perceive has travelled to us across space in packets of parallel lines.

In general, rectilinear rays are man made. If the room where the candle has been lighted has a small window with the curtain left undrawn, the light from the window at night appears outside as a straight beam. Obviously that is because, while almost the whole of each successive sphere of radiation falling upon the inner surfaces of the room is there reflected or scattered or absorbed, the part that falls on the window can go on; it takes the form of a longitudinal beam, its cross-section the shape of the window-frame. The revolving rays from a lighthouse are a familiar example; different sections of the continuous train of wave-spheres, formed inside the lantern, being allowed to emerge outside in a succession, usually after being concentrated by reflectors and lenses.

Similarly with the astronomer's telescope: it cuts a small circle into an advancing front of spherical waves; this core meets the object-glass and emerges on the other side as a rectilinear beam, the rest passing on outside the telescope until stopped. A notional straight line may be imagined for mathematical purposes, crossing space from a star to the observatory: but this is fictional and does not portray anything that actually happens. A recent text-book says, "There is no such thing in nature as a linear wave of light."

2

That radiation is emitted as a series of expanding spheres gives us the simple explanation of the law of the inverse square. Why is it that the intensity of light, for example, at any point-instant is always found to have diminished in the inverse ratio of the square of the distance travelled from the source of emission? Why is it never in simple proportion to the distance; or as the cube of the distance; or any other multiple or fraction? This is no mysterious mathematical rule, discovered empirically and to be accepted as given by nature. It necessarily follows from the fact that the area of the surface of any sphere depends upon the square of its radius.[1] The intensity of a light-wave decreases as it spreads over a larger area—that is to say in proportion to the increase in the area of the sphere's surface. That area increases according to the square of the distance; therefore the intensity must decrease according to the square of the distance.

The same rule necessarily holds in every case of expanding spheres: for example in the diffusion of sound in the atmosphere.

[1] The formula is $4\pi r^2$ where r is the radius. The other terms being constants, r is the only variable.

3

A pattern is related to something not itself. A wave is a pattern, related to a volume of water, or of air, or whatever it may be. The wave travels, but the material does not travel. Between a tuning-fork and the ear an air-wave moves forward, but the air itself does not: what happens is that the atoms or molecules of the air at any particular spot swing to and fro, perhaps a thousandth of an inch or less, through alternate compression and rarefaction. The same principle applies on the surface of the sea. There is a clear distinction between a sound-wave and a wind in the air, or a water-wave and a current in the sea. A wave has been well described as a 'moving configuration.'

But in the case of light, or other electromagnetic radiation, it is at present generally assumed by physicists that it is the energy itself that travels. A widely-used text-book already quoted says that "the most important property of the electromagnetic waves is that they convey energy." This theory of 'conveyance' has to be postulated because nothing is offered as the material of which the wave may be a configuration.

The scheme now submitted does not fall back upon any such *ad hoc* differentiation, between waves of light (or other radiation) and waves in air or in water. All are regarded as conforming to one of the standard models of nature.

Energy, being a continuum, cannot move, or be conveyed, from place to place. It can change from a state of quiescence to a state of activity and vice versa. But that happens there—where it is. As in the other cases, the motion of the wave is a motion of a state of the material and not of the material itself.

We may picture the actual process as being perhaps something of this kind. An oscillating point sets going a continuous series of spheres of activation in the surrounding quiescent ether. Owing to the oscillation, the spheres are not exactly concentric: each of the spheres in the succession has its center slightly out of the line between the centers of the one before and the one after. If this were so, the spheres would be emitted in a series of layers, and these layers would not be suppositions but physically real. It is this alternation of eccentric layers which gives rise to the wave.

The process of activation would appear to consist, then, in each layer in turn changing, under the impact from the wave approaching, from the quiescent state to the active. It next activates the layer surrounding it, in an equal degree, and then itself relapses into quiescence. This is repeated, at the speed of the velocity of light, continuously, so long as the effect of the original impact endures.

A process such as this would account for the fact that velocity is dependent upon the nature of the medium, not on the strength of the impact. A bright light travels no faster than a dim one, a loud sound no faster than a soft one, because the mechanism of transmission in each case works at a speed specific to the character of the medium. If it were the energy itself that travelled it would be difficult to explain why a large emission of energy should travel no faster than a small one.

The bearing of the Law of the Conservation of Energy upon a scheme such as that suggested here is a point of primary importance: it can however be more conveniently discussed later, in a different context.

One further point may be added here. Text-books of physics tell us that "if a plane wave of light is allowed to fall on an opaque screen perforated with a very small aperture, the point on the wave front not cut off by the screen acts as a center of disturbance, which spreads out into the space behind the screen, and a card placed there will be illuminated over an area many times greater than that of the aperture." This is further evidence of the existence of a physical ether capable of being activated. A 'center of disturbance'—disturbance of what?

PARTICLES 1

Since the discovery of the particle structure of matter we have been gradually accustoming ourselves to the idea that objects, solid in relation to us, are not solid, in the same sense, in themselves. We cannot pass through a window-pane without breaking it, but light from the sun passes through almost as though it were not there. The wall of a room is solid enough if we knock against it: to waves from broadcasting stations it is as transparent as the window is to sunlight. Difficult as it has been to reconcile with daily experience, we realize on reflection that the objects about us—our own bodies, the rocks of the mountains, all material things—are made up of atoms, each atom an organized system of particles, and each particle in a state of extremely rapid motion.

We have arrived, historically, at the particle along a course of discovery which began with familiar objects, passed on to chemical molecules, from them to atoms and finally to the particles. Consequently we think of a particle as much smaller than the others which have preceded it, but essentially of the same kind—as an exceedingly minute object of a definite shape and size. An ether theory, however, approaching the subject from the opposite end, may reach quite a different conception.

Beginning with a universal featureless ocean of quiescent energy, it may conceive waves of activation, which are 'moving configurations' of the energic ether. But it may conceive as well the formation of particles, which would also be patterns, like the waves, but of a different kind. While waves are diffused, and move forward autonomously in expanding spheres, the particles are discrete and coherent; and the activation manifests itself in motion, and in forces of attraction and repulsion, that are internal.

2

Atomic physicists have found a number of different kinds of particles. At the 1949 meeting of the British Association, Dr. N. Kemmer, of Trinity College, Cambridge, said to the Mathematical Section, "Modern physics recognizes at least ten distinct elementary particles, and it is probable that more will be discovered." Dr. J. Robert Oppenheimer, Director of the Institute for Advanced Study at Princeton, agrees that the number of particles now generally recognized is ten; he adds five more as probables.

It is known that different particles have different degrees of stability. The free life of positrons, for instance, is found to be very short: they disappear almost as soon as they are freed. Other kinds may last for periods of minutes, hours, days, years, centuries; or to perpetuity, unless broken up by outside agencies.

In the early studies of the structure of the atom a resemblance was seen to the solar system: the nucleus was the sun; one, two, or many particles moved around it like the planets. And it was natural to suppose that all particles were more or less uniform, and that they were circling in orbits and spinning on their axes. It is now plain that they are not uniform. Newton, holding the corpuscular theory of light, assumed that the corpuscle had some kind of structure. Oppenheimer says that physicists nowadays regard electrons, and other kinds of particles, as being 'composite.' If our imagination could probe inside the particle, as it has probed inside the atom, we might well find that the constructions are as varied and as complicated in the one case as they have been found to be in the other.

We can conceive particles consisting of two sub-particles, revolving round each other like binary stars, or of several sub-particles, the number varying perhaps as greatly as the number of particles in atoms. Or a particle might consist of a hollow sphere of active energy round a core of quiescent. The path of a particle within the atom might be a circle or an ellipse; but it might also be in other patterns: it is believed that sometimes the path of an electron may be in the figure of a rosette. Or a particle might not move at all relatively to the atomic nucleus, but vibrate; or both move and vibrate, and possibly spin as well. The masses, charges, and spins of different kinds of particles are also known to differ.

We must assume that, as in the case of ether-waves, if there is such a process of activation it must attain a certain minimum to be effective. (Here again the question will arise whether Planck's constant *h* has any relevance.)

The minimum may be reached and a particle may come into existence, but its structure may not be viable. The particle may be one of the many kinds which have been found by observation and experiment to be unstable: they may disappear the moment after their formation or with no long interval.

We conceive the particles to be moving, inside the atom—in whatever way or ways they may move—in an environment of quiescent ether. That this is not itself thrown into the active state would be because the strength of the impact was below the critical minimum.

3

Wherever and whenever the requisite conditions obtain we may suppose particles forming in the quiescent ether. What those conditions may be we have no conception; and we may never reach any conception, since quiescent ether is imperceptible and indescribable. In nature we are familiar with the process of crystallization, as in the formation of ice and snow, or of quartzes. In certain liquid chemical mixtures crystallization occurs when the matrix has reached a critical point in temperature and pressure combined: at one moment the molecules are not arranged but diffused; at another moment they are arranged, in a regular geometrical pattern specific to the material, and are consolidated. In some cases a catalyst will stimulate the process. What may be the ether conditions, equivalent to temperature and pressure or to catalysis, which will bring about the formation of particles we do not know. But there is no ground for asserting that such a process is impossible. Analogy from elsewhere and inference from observed phenomena may lead us to think it not only possible, but probable. This may be a normal and constant process. It may indeed be the fundamental process of the physical universe.

Physicists have in fact begun in recent years to speak of the 'creation and destruction of matter,' through the appearance and disappearance of particles. In the course of a series of broadcasts on the B.B.C., since published as a book, Mr. Fred Hoyle says that this idea had been put forward by a German scientist, P. Jordan, and by the Cambridge scientists, H. Bondi and T. Gold, and that he himself, approaching the problem along different lines, had reached almost identical conclusions. He says: "From time to time people ask where the created material comes from. Well, it does not come from anywhere. Material simply appears—it is created. At one time the various atoms composing the material do not exist and at a later time they do. This may seem a very strange idea and I agree that it is, but in science it does not matter how strange an idea may seem so long as it works—that is to say, so long as the idea can be expressed in a precise form and so long as its consequences are found to be in agreement with observation. In any case the whole idea of creation is queer. In the older theories all the material in the Universe is supposed to have appeared at one instant of time, the whole creation process taking the form of one big bang. For myself I find this idea very much queerer than continuous creation."

It is doubtful whether such a theory as this could possibly be accepted by science as a final answer to the question: it could certainly not be accepted by philosophy, and it is rejected by commonsense. There must be some kind of matrix from which the particles may emerge and into which they may disappear—as flakes of ice appear here and there in a river when it falls below freezing-point, and disappear when it rises above it. The flakes do not come out of nothing—"at one time they do not exist and at a later time they do," as Hoyle would say. They emerge from a matrix which is of an order at once like and unlike themselves—like, in that both are of the same chemical composition; unlike, in that one is in the solid state and the other in the liquid. So the conception here put forward is that energy in the active state, arranged into a particle, emerges from energy in the quiescent state, which has no arrangement: it may, or may not, afterwards relapse into quiescence—that is, into inertia.

Similarly with the example of a flash of lightning. The phenomenon must be accepted as given physical fact: it is proved to be so by the effects upon houses, trees, animals, people, that we often observe. But we cannot conceive that the lightning comes out of nothing and consists of nothing. If it is 'something,' that something must be of the same order of physical reality as the objects that a flash strikes and destroys, otherwise it could not make contact with them and affect them. It follows that the 'something' at one time does not produce the phenomena of lightning; at a particular moment it does produce them; and at the next moment it produces them no longer. In other words there must be a matrix or medium which physically exists before, during, and after the observed event. If this something thus exists continuously, we can hardly escape the conclusion that it must be in one state before the event, in a different state during the event, and again in a different state—presumably the same as the first—after the event.

4

It has been discovered in recent years that 'interstellar space' is not empty, but contains flying electrons, atoms, molecules, and dust. It is now thought that, in the total, as much matter may exist in the universe in this form as in all the stars. This is evidently a fact of the first importance in cosmology. It could be explained without difficulty if such dispersed forms of matter were normal ether products. There would then be no need for the questionable theory that has been offered, that these immense quantities of particles, atoms, and dust have been scattered from time to time, in the course of the history of the universe, by the explosions of stars.

We conceive, then, vast numbers of individual particles constantly forming in any part of the ocean of quiescent ether. Those whose internal structures so require will associate with other particles, of the same or different types, to form atoms. Similarly the atoms will combine to form molecules. Later the molecules may be aggregated into stars or other stellar objects. We may say that matter is clotted ether.

Some of the particles are abortive. They come into existence, but their structures are defective for survival: they prove to be evanescent or insufficiently stable; sooner or later they disappear. Others endure for long periods, and form the stable elements that we know, constituting gases, liquids, and solids that are permanent.

If this is indeed the creative method at the cosmological level, we find here the same process—of trial and error, of the survival of the fittest to survive and the disappearance of the unfit—as we know to prevail at the biological level. The principle of evolution would again be manifest as the law that governs the development of the world.

MOMENTUM 1

Since the universe operates physically only through motion—something being at one time at one place, relatively to other things, and at another time at another place —it might be expected that everyone would be interested to know, if possible, what it is that causes—or allows—or enables this motion to happen. But it appears that, at present, this is not so. Physicists in general are not interested.

In particular, on this question of motion, one of the scientists to whom this essay was submitted in draft wrote as follows: "I think my fundamental estrangement from your general approach, which would probably be shared by most physicists, is that I do not feel your need to find a picturable *cause* for phenomena. What I want, and what physics gives, is a *description* which shows them as related but not as effects of hypothetical causes. For one thing, how can you decide what needs a cause and what would happen without one? If a bullet goes on moving, is a cause necessary to keep it going or would a cause be necessary to stop it? I do not see how one can decide except by seeing which assumption is more effective in establishing relations between phenomena. The ancients thought that in the absence of a cause it would be at rest and that a cause was necessary to keep it moving. Newton thought that in the absence of a cause it would go on moving with uniform velocity and that a cause was necessary to change its velocity. Einstein thinks that in the absence of a cause it will move with uniform acceleration and that a cause is necessary to change its acceleration. And so on. We choose the assumption which subsequently provides the best account of the relations between phenomena. Consequently I do not feel the need of an ether to explain things which I am willing to accept as data to be ordered into a rational system."

The insistent curiosity of the philosopher will not allow him to be satisfied with this.

The answer to the particular question put to me—as to the cause of a bullet starting to move, continuing to move, being accelerated and stopping—should be, I think, that we are dealing here, not with one event, but with four separable events. A different combination of causes is needed to account for each of them: one to start the bullet, a second to sustain its flight, a third to accelerate (if it could be accelerated), and a fourth to end it. The adventures of the bullet are events actually happening in the universe. An explanation is either right or wrong: those are right which observation and experiment will show can "account for the relations between phenomena"; those are wrong which prove to be inconsistent with them. Until a right explanation is forthcoming the problem remains unsolved; but we are not therefore obliged to desist from trying to find the solution. Max Planck took exception, as he says, "to the view (a very popular one these days, and certainly a very plausible one on the face of it) that a problem in physics merits examination only if it is established in advance that a definite answer to it can be obtained."

2

Let us come to close quarters with the question of momentum.

Consider as an illustration the incident of David and Goliath: "And David put his hand in his bag, and took thence a stone, and slang it, and smote the Philistine in his forehead, that the stone sunk into his forehead; and he fell upon his face to the earth." I ask—What happened between the place where David was and the place where Goliath was, and between the time when the stone left the sling and the time when it struck the Philistine, so that he was stunned and then killed?

Newton said, "Every body continues in a state of rest, or of uniform motion in a straight line . . . ," but he did not attempt to discuss the Why or the How. He did not consider it his function to fashion hypotheses; he was content to "propose principles of Motion." He did not regard that, however, as the end of the matter; he would "leave their Causes to be found out." Whitehead thinks that universities should chant in their halls, as a "first article in the creed of science," that motion continues 'naturally.' Text-books of physics tell us that an object moves because it 'has kinetic energy'; or because of the 'metric properties of space.' But when I examine in turn these words—'naturally,' 'possesses,' 'momentum,' 'kinetic,' 'properties,' 'space'—each one seems, in this connection, to signify nothing at all. All are purely scholastic, in that they are linguistic terms used as though they were factors in physical events.

Scientists, then, give no answer, and usually nowadays do not attempt, or even wish to give an answer, to any Socratic gadfly who persists in asking such questions as What actually occurred between David's hand and Goliath's head at that particular moment? They try to shake off the gadfly, like the Athenians in the market-place. But we see now that Socrates was right to be insistent, and that something may come of such questionings in the end.

3

Action at a distance without contiguity having been excluded, we must postulate the existence of something, in between David and Goliath, which will sustain the stone against the downward pull of gravity and convey it during its flight. It cannot be 'space,' for space is not something that exists. It is not, of course, the air: apart from winds, the air does not impel but impedes. What we are looking for must be something that can produce effects on its own account, that is itself active; otherwise it would not serve the purpose. We might perhaps be driven to imagine some new agency that has no relation to anything in our experience, and rest there; in other words we should have to admit defeat and give up the inquiry. But if we wish to escape that failure, we may consent to consider afresh whether there is anything that is within our experience, recognized to be physically real, which might prove to be the agency that we seek. For there must be an agency, otherwise the event could not have happened. By this process of exhaustion we are left with only Energy.

4

When we examine the word Moves, as used colloquially, we shall find that it too is misleading: not because it is scholastic—it certainly denotes a reality; but because it is ambiguous.

We say "the bird moves through the air," and we also say "the bullet moves through the air," as though the two events had the same character. But there is a fundamental difference between them. The bird moves because the organs and muscles of its body, directed by its mind, enable it to beat with wings upon the atmosphere and to propel itself forward; it can turn this way or that, or stop its movements and alight; the bird is autonomous. But the bullet is passive; it is no different after it has been fired off than before; it has not thereby come to 'possess' anything; it does not 'carry' or 'convey' anything at all. The cause of the flight must be looked for in something other than the bullet itself. If we wished to speak precisely we ought to say that *the bird moves,* but that *the bullet is moved.*

Moved by what? For the reasons given, nothing would be there to do it if not an energic ether.

5

In another respect the word Moves is misleading, again confusing together two different things.

In every case of momentum there are two distinct phases—one in which the movement is initiated, the other in which it is continued. A ball thrown in a game or a stone cast from a sling, a bullet fired from a gun, a runner jumping over a hurdle—in each case the impetus is given by one set of causes and the movement is carried on by another. At the moment when the hand releases its hold on the ball or the sling lets go the stone, when the expanding gases in the barrel of the gun no longer affect the bullet, or when the feet of the runner cease to press against the ground, a different situation arises. Those factors disappear completely. It looks as though the object continued 'of its own accord'; but if we say that we say nothing.

In Newton's law a distinction between initiation and continuance is implied, but is not made explicit. He deals with two cases—one of a body which is in a state of rest and is made to change that state by outside forces impressed upon it; the other a body which is already moving and continues to move when no longer affected by those forces. The key words are 'impressed' and 'continues.' But he does not discuss the distinction between the two. Indeed we do not usually realize that there is such a distinction, or that, if there is, it has any special significance. Closer inquiry will show that here is the essence of the whole matter.

A theory of a Two-State Ether would describe any such event as follows. An object, being a particle or a system of particles, is set in motion, relatively to the point of initiation: it makes an impact on the portion of quiescent ether that is adjacent. If and when the impact is of a strength that exceeds the requisite minimum, this quiescent ether is also activated. The first phase, that of initiation, is thereby completed.

The surrounding ether then activates in turn the quiescent ether beyond, which likewise affects a further area; and so on, in sequence, so long as the process lasts. If the stream of activation is strong enough, it may carry along in its course free objects that are within its influence, including the one that caused the original impact. Itself dynamic, it carries forward the passive objects. This is the second, the continuing phase: it goes on independently of the first.

6

I will now offer several illustrations, drawn from various aspects of familiar experience or from scientific observation, in order to expand and, I hope, clarify, that summary statement. I will leave till later an inquiry into the possible mechanism of such a process.

1. Two balls are lying on a billiard-table. A player strikes or pushes the first ball with his cue; it strikes the second ball full in the center; thereupon it stops, and the second ball travels forward in the same line of direction and with the same velocity.

The explanation that would at present be given is somewhat as follows. The player possesses in his body a store of 'potential energy,' derived from elements in his food and drink, from the atmosphere and from sunlight. Some of this energy he now releases to operate a muscular effort of his arm. From the arm it is transmitted down the cue and enters the ball, causing it to roll along the table. When the first ball is obstructed by the second, it 'gives up its energy' to the other, so 'transferring the momentum' and causing the second ball to travel forward instead of itself.

An ether theory would deny the existence of any 'store of potential energy,' capable of being 'released,' like water from a cistern when a tap is turned on. It would also regard as meaningless, when applied to a passive object like a billiard-ball, such terms as 'giving up' or 'transferring.' It would describe the situation under inquiry as consisting, in the first instance, of the presence of an autonomous human being and of a billiard-table with two balls resting on it, together with the universal ether continuum: the earth's gravity is also a constant factor, holding down the man and the table to the floor of the room and the balls to the table. The man has the capacity of muscular movement, made possible by chemical materials and processes and electrical impulses as constituents of his body. This being the situation, when the man moves his arm and propels the first ball with his cue, we conceive that this movement activates the quiescent ether which permeates and surrounds the ball. The resultant of the forces so set up together with gravity continuously operating, sets the ball rolling. This initial phase is completed when the movement of the player's arm stops.

In the second phase the ball is kept rolling by the sequence of activations of further areas of quiescent ether: this goes on, independently of the player, for so long as the strength of the activations does not fall below the requisite minimum. A different situation is now brought about by the presence of the second ball in the path of the first. It may be that, for the purposes of the game, the player has skilfully regulated his effort so that his ball just reaches the other and 'kisses' it, without stirring it from its place. That is to say the strength of the series of impacts has been exhausted precisely at that point: the last impact cannot overcome the pull of gravity which has been holding the second ball where it is. In that case the process ends then. But if the original stroke was harder than that, the first ball will be stopped by the obstruction of the second—caused by its 'weight,' *i.e.*, the effect of gravity on its mass; this, however, will be overcome by the continuing sequence of activations, which will set the second ball rolling instead of the first. If the originating impulse had been still stronger, or caused by a continuing pushing movement of the cue on the ball, then the first ball would make a momentary pause when it comes in contact with the second, but would then 'follow on' after it, being carried forward again, but for a less distance than the other.

2. The distinction between an initiating and a continuing movement may be visualized if we were to watch a pair of horses straining to start a heavily loaded wagon. It may be that their most strenuous efforts do not succeed in making it move, and that it is only when part of the load has been taken off that the wheels can be made to turn. But once set going the wagon will roll along easily, with little effort from the horses. Their powerful pull is one phase, travelling along 'under its own impetus' is another.

3. Consider next a case of circular motion, not unlike that of David's sling but with differences.

In the Olympic Games and sometimes at other athletic sports, especially in Scotland, one item in the program is Throwing the Hammer. What was originally no doubt an ordinary heavy long-handled hammer has been conventionalized into a sixteen-pound weight attached to a strong wire with a looped handle, the whole being four feet in length. Each competitor, in turn, standing in a marked circle of specified size, grasps the handle and whirls the weight round and round, releasing it at what he judges to be the right moment. The winner is the one who, while keeping within the ring, is able to give the greatest velocity to the circling weight and so throw it the longest distance.

We watch the athlete setting the weight swinging through the air, turning himself round and round and whirling it faster and faster. With every revolution the pull upon his body gets stronger and stronger: if he waits too long before letting go he will be dragged out of the ring in spite of all his resistance and even thrown to the ground. What is it that is dragging him about? It is not a differential equation or a statistical concept! It is something very factual, entirely real. It is Energy itself, stirred from rest into action.

If we ask why it is that, when the handle is released, the weight flies off at a tangent and does not go on circling, we need not have recourse for an answer to some question-begging phrase like "the effect of centrifugal force." We may reply that the athlete had provided an initiating movement by whirling the weight round and round, and that, when the impact on the quiescent ether had become sufficient, a continuous series of activations had been set up. If we picture the movement of the weight in a single revolution as a circle, and take any two points in it very close together and join them by a straight line, then the direction of the activation process, at the moment when the weight reaches the points, would be along that line. But the weight cannot be projected along that line because the restraining pull of the wire prevents it. If, however, the wire was released at that moment it would be. This applies to any point in the circle. Consequently, whenever the athlete lets go of the handle the weight will fly off at a tangent.

The distance that the so-called hammer will be hurled through the air before it drops to the ground under the pull of gravity, will depend upon the strength of the originating impacts; and that in turn depends upon the mass of the hammer combined with the velocity that the athlete had succeeded in imparting to it.

4. A further example may be drawn from an experience common among residents in London or other cities with underground railways.

In a crowded carriage a passenger is standing up, holding on to a strap fixed above him. When the train is leaving a station the straphanger feels himself being pulled forward; there is a strain on the muscles of his arm. When the carriages have gathered speed this strain ceases. As they approach the next station and the brakes are applied, he feels himself being impelled forward but held back by his strap; the strain reappears, but in the opposite direction. If, owing to some accident on the line, the train were to be suddenly stopped, we know that all the standing passengers would be wrenched away from their straps and hurled violently forward, suffering perhaps severe injuries. All this would be attributed to the 'impetus' of the train. But what is impetus?

We would say that here the initiating motion is supplied by the engine. The continuing movement is caused partly by the engine, using enough power to overcome the running friction, but mainly by the activation of the quiescent ether which permeates the interior of the tunnel and all its contents. In the first phase, while the train is beginning to move and before the activation is fully effective, the straphanger is being pulled simultaneously in two directions: one by the force of gravity, which tends to keep him stationary where he is, relative to the surface of the earth; the other by the strap, which, attached to the carriage and being pulled forwards by the engine, would carry him along with it. Hence the strain on his arm. In the second phase, when the activation has been established and the train is running along easily with little help from the engine, the strain is relaxed. This is because the downward pull of gravity has been sufficiently overcome by the horizontal pull, or push, of the activation. Everything in the train is equally affected —its furnishings, the bodies of the passengers, the atoms and molecules of the air. The passenger feels that he can now let go of the strap without fear of being jerked off his balance by the acceleration of the train. In the third phase, when the brakes are applied and the carriages are being slowed down, for a few seconds the effect of the activating process continues. If the train were stopped dead it is during those few seconds, and then only, that the passengers would be thrown about. In ordinary circumstances the straphanger would need to take hold of his strap again, in order to resist the tendency now of his body, under the ether stress, still to go forward, while the railway-carriage is being checked and stopped by the friction caused by the brakes.

In the early theories the ether was supposed to be ultratenuous and very weak; strong enough to carry radiations of light, but probably not for anything else. Substances, on the other hand, were looked upon as absolutely solid and heavy. It is still difficult for commonsense to imagine it possible for a train of a dozen steel carriages, with some hundreds of passengers, to be carried along, at a high speed, merely by some kind of ether activity. Nevertheless on reflection we realize that railway trains and human bodies are nothing more than aggregations of atoms, which are themselves mostly 'volumes of emptiness'; also that the power embodied in any single atom is immense. (The complete destruction of one ton of uranium by fission releases as much energy as the burning of three million tons of coal.) And it is not difficult to imagine that the same energy may exist outside the atoms as well as inside; may indeed be universally diffused, although not continuously active. If so, there would be, in that tunnel, enough energy and of a potency so colossal that, were it all to be brought into full activity, everything there would be turned in an instant into white-hot gas, followed by the most devastating earthquake ever known. So far from ether not being strong enough to move a train, it would have to be stirred to only an infinitesimal degree to supply all the mechanical needs of mankind, now and always.

5. The earth itself, as it circles round the sun, is being upheld and impelled by the same ultimate force. Once having been set in motion—as to which there are various hypotheses—it rolls on by the activation of the ether within and around it through the effect of its own impact. It is an example of Newton's Third Law of Motion: "To every action there is always opposed an equal reaction." The globe as it rolls evokes, from the limitless

ocean of quiescent ether always there waiting, a strip, so to speak, of ether activation. This carries on the 'moving configurations' of particles and waves which constitute the globe. When it has passed, each portion of the activated ether relapses into quiescence. The process would carry the planet forward in a straight line, relatively to other astral bodies, were it not that the constant gravitational pull of the sun constrains it into an ellipse. The mass of the planet and the velocity of its motion are sufficient to ensure that the impacts shall never fail and the activations never end—the motion is perpetual. And so with all the astral bodies.

We mark once more the fundamental difference between the earlier theories of an ether and that now presented. With them the ether would necessarily obstruct the movement of the stars and planets: here the ether is the very cause of the movement itself.

7

The reason is now plain why, if a Two-State Ether of this character exists, the experiment of Michelson and Morley was bound to give a null result.

Setting out to establish a standard of absolute motion relative to the ether, they began by taking it for granted that the earth was one thing and the ether another, and that the earth travelled 'in' and moved 'through' the ether. But that is not the situation that we are now supposing: from the present standpoint the purpose they had in view is seen to be unattainable because it rests upon an assumption which is unfounded.

We can say that the earth is *in* its atmosphere because the one is separable from the other. A boundary, however irregular, exists between the earth's surface and the air: between the molecules of water, rock, soil, and vegetation and the atoms and molecules of the atmospheric gases and water-vapor. Standing on the earth we can feel the wind moving across it; a tornado will blow down trees and houses. But there is nothing comparable in the case of the earth and the ether. There is no boundary. Both are fundamentally the same. There is no point, inside the earth or outside it, at which the ether is not present. Particular portions of it, at any particular moment, may be quiescent and undifferentiated, and other portions active and differentiated; but are equally ether. We mislead ourselves therefore when, in this context, we use the prepositions 'in' and 'through.' A thing cannot be *in* itself, or move *through* itself.

If, on board ship, we watch a wave travelling alongside, ought we to say that 'the wave is in the water' or that 'the water is in the wave'? The one would be as true as the other. It is better to say neither, but that the wave *is* water and the water *is* wave. The wave is water because that is what it is made of: the water is wave when that is its pattern. (In the same way matter is energy, and is always energy—because that is what it is made of. Energy is matter: but not always—only when it is organized into particles or combinations of particles. It may be quiescent; or it may be in a wave pattern; or, as will be suggested later, in what may be termed a motor pattern; or possibly in other patterns not known to us.)

We can locate the earth in relation to the sun—one aggregate of particles of active ether in relation to another. But we cannot locate either earth or sun in relation to the ether as a whole because that constitutes and permeates both of them.

The same applies to all the factors in the Michelson-Morley apparatus. Not only to the actual apparatus—the interferometer, made of metal and glass—but also to the intervals between the point of light-emission and the mirrors, and to the light-waves themselves. There can be no question of the material parts of the apparatus travelling, with the earth, *through* the ether, and of the light-waves being loose and not doing so. All are equally ether. They are all of a piece.

In point of fact, physicists, I am assured, do not hold that the Michelson-Morley experiment proves that there is no ether, but only that *there is no ether with properties expressible by the laws of mechanics.* This would still give room for an ether which, in its quiescent state, is not conceived as possessing those properties. On the contrary the experiment may be held rather to support a speculation that an ether, in the last analysis, is the only physical thing that does exist. It is because the ether constitutes the substance of the earth itself equally with its environment that it cannot provide any points of reference from which to measure the motion between them, the existence of that motion being, nevertheless, a given physical fact.

GRAVITATION (I) 1

"Although gravity," says Whittaker, "was the first of the forces of nature to be brought within the domain of exact science and represented by a mathematical formula, and although a prodigious amount of highly successful work has been done in the development of the theory, yet the fundamental physical problems connected with it are almost as perplexing to-day as they have ever been."

For any fresh approach the one firm starting-point is the established fact that a gravitational pull varies in strength inversely as the square of the distance of the object pulled from the gravitational center. When discussing the application of the inverse-square rule to radiation we emphasized that it was a consequence of the fact that the area of the surface of a sphere is dependent upon the square of its radius. If radiation were propagated in a series of expanding spherical waves, then the intensity of the radiation, at any point-instant, must necessarily be less than at the point and time of emission in proportion to the square of the distance travelled. The inverse-square rule also applies in the case of sound in the atmosphere, and we attribute this to the fact that the propagation of sound is another case of expanding spherical waves. If in mathematics and in radiation and in sound, we find this association between the inverse-square rule and expanding spheres, it is legitimate to infer, unless there is reason to suppose the contrary, that, when we come to gravitation and find the same rule prevailing there, it is because the same connection exists. And since, in the other cases, the result is a wave-motion, it will be a wave-motion in this case also. The conclusion is indicated that gravity is propagated in expanding spherical waves.

That this is so is now generally accepted by physicists. Relativity theory requires the existence of gravitational waves. As long ago as 1923, Eddington discussed, from the mathematical standpoint, 'electromagnetic gravitational waves' and the 'electromagnetic mode of propagation of gravitational influence.' It would follow that the propagation of gravity must be a time-process. Newton held the contrary—that it was instantaneous; but it is now regarded as established that this is not the case. Whittaker says, "The problem was finally solved by the discovery of the gravitational waves of the general theory of relativity; the most recent work on the subject makes it clear that the speed of propagation of gravitation is the same as that of light." [2]

2

We look for a point of emission. In the case of radiation, the wave-motion has been found to originate in atomic oscillation. The spectroscope gives proof of this. It analyses sunlight into a band of light of graduated color, crossed by dark lines. These lines are found to form groups, which when separated out, correspond exactly with similar

[2] Faraday gave a lecture, a hundred years ago, with the title "On the Possible Relation of Gravity to Electricity." In it he described his experiments to find a relation, which all failed; nevertheless, he said, "they do not shake my strange feeling of the existence of a relation." (J. Bronowski, *The Listener,* March 2, 1950.)

spectral groups obtained from specimens of terrestrial gases and metals made incandescent. We conclude that the light of the sun proceeds from atoms of the same chemical elements as produce the same spectral lines in our laboratories. And if the mechanism of light emission is atomic oscillation here, it will also be so in the sun.

The atoms of any particular element in an incandescent star must have their own specific wave-rhythm; otherwise the distinctive character of the radiation of each element could not be retained and produce a separable and identifiable line-group in the spectrum. But it is evident that the radiation from all the individual atoms in the star, of all the elements, are aggregated together to produce the wave-packets characteristic of the star. The wave impulses radiating from the single atoms combine to form the large expanding spherical waves of ether-activation which travel across the universe. It seems that the expanding spheres, when they touch one another, unite into larger ones: as soap-bubbles, floating in air or on water, join to form larger bubbles.

If there are gravitation-waves, similarly emanating from atomic oscillations, we may expect that there will be an amalgamation. "When Newton," we are told, "suspected that gravity might be accounted for by supposing that every particle in the universe attracted every other particle with a force which varied directly as their masses and inversely as the square of the distance between them, he was held up by a mathematical difficulty; . . . he could not for a long time calculate how the small forces due to the individual particles of a sphere such as the earth would combine into a resultant force exerted by the whole sphere." It was nearly ten years before that purely mechanical difficulty was overcome: ever since then it has been accepted that the gravity of an astral body is such a resultant of individual infinitesimal atomic forces.

3

It seems therefore that radiation and gravitation are similar in the following respects:

1. Both are subject to the inverse-square rule.
2. Both are propagated by spherical waves expanding from a center.
3. The waves of both kinds travel with the same velocity.
4. Both originate in the oscillation of atoms.
5. In both cases individual infinitesimal waves are aggregated into spheres that are large, and often immense.

We can hardly escape the conclusion that gravitation is a form of radiation, that it is part of the electromagnetic mechanism of the universe.

But if this is so, the question at once presents itself—How can an emission outwards result in an attraction inwards?

Here we connect with the general problem of the mechanism of motion, to which we now turn.

THE MECHANISM OF MOTION 1

But I would pause for a moment to take note of the point at which the triumphant march of physical discovery, never more remarkable than during the last fifty or sixty years, is, for the time being, halted.

Man had always accepted the familiar world revealed by the senses as what it seemed to be. He was aware of the earth and the sky, of heat and fire, light and colors, sound and scent, of substance, weight and motion. But what lay behind and beneath all these he did not know, and seldom stayed to ask.

It is hardly three centuries since the achievements of the pioneers of modern science began to show substantial results. Light was found to be, not simple but composite. It was analysed into a spectrum graduated into different wave-lengths, from violet at one end to red at the other—the violet waves being about half as long as the red. It was this difference of wave-lengths which, when light passed into the eye, gave us the different sensations that we call colors. Next it was discovered that, beyond each end of the visible spectrum, there existed waves of other lengths, the ultra-violet and the infra-red and radiant heat, all these now familiar through their therapeutic uses. Then, suddenly, in the short period between 1887 and 1898, Hertz, Röntgen, Becquerel and the Curies made their remarkable discoveries. These again extended the known wave-band at both ends: much shorter than the ultra-violet were the x-rays and the gamma-rays from radioactive substances; and, much longer than the infra-red and the heat waves, were the Hertzian waves, now used in broadcasting and radar. At the extreme ends of the band, the longest of the whole series are about a million-million times as long as the shortest. Somewhere midway is the minute part of the wave-band which is the light that we see.

For the purposes of this essay the first point of interest here is the astonishing difference in the phenomena, as we experience them, which proceed from the same origin. Looked at from our side—broadcasting, heat, light, colors, x-ray photography, gamma-ray penetration—each seems very different from the others; looked at from nature's side, the difference between them is simply a matter of varying lengths in a single system of electromagnetic waves.

The second point of interest is the unlikelihood that at this moment of time everything in this field that there was to be discovered has been discovered. That, no doubt, may possibly be the case; it may be that the middle of the twentieth century will prove to have been the precise moment when all the knowledge there was to gain had been won. But this is hardly likely; and it is made the more improbable by the fact that in two universal matters —momentum and gravity—we are still almost completely ignorant. We can measure momentum and we can measure gravity; but as to their causes—apart from the recent recognition that, in gravitation, some kind of radiating waves are a factor—we must admit, if we are frank, that we know nothing at all.

2

Considering first the momentum of material objects, it seems that the ether-activation is not of the wave pattern, consequent upon an atomic oscillation: the inverse-square rule, always associated with a spherical wave process, does not appear. Nor do we find any sign of the particle pattern: in none of the cases of impact and impetus are particles as such playing a causal part. We are obliged to inquire, therefore, whether there may not exist some other form, or forms, of activation which have not yet been distinguished—perhaps because not yet looked for—by observation and experiment.

Such a situation has often occurred from time to time in the history of science. In Dalton's day it was supposed that all atoms were alike, except in size and weight; it is now known that they are made up in at least ninety-seven different ways. Until recently, all atoms of the same chemical element were thought to be identical; it is now known that isotopes constantly occur. When the structure of the atom was first discovered only two kinds of particles were recognized—the positively charged and the negatively: there are believed at present to be at least ten and possibly fifteen. We have the example again of the spectrum of visible light, which was assumed to be the whole of the wave-band: only after a long time were vast extensions revealed. We need not hesitate to suggest, therefore, that fresh discoveries are possible; as they are certainly needed if we are to find solutions for these two outstanding problems.

It is conceivable, indeed, that when we assume ether itself to be homogeneous, and speak of it as *the* ether, that also may be mistaken. Perhaps two kinds of ether, or several, may later be discovered, mingled together but each producing its own order of phenomena. To inquire along that line, however, would obviously be unprofitable; we have nothing to go upon, and at present not even a starting-point.

In the particular case of momentum, if we hold that it is caused by ether activation, but not in either the wave or the particle form, it is natural to ask in what other form, at present unknown, it might be. When David whirls his sling and then lets go of one of the thongs and the stone flies off; when the billiard-player propels his ball; when the horses get the wagon rolling; when the engine-driver starts his train—in all such cases an initiating movement causes an ether impact, impact sets up impetus, and impetus gives momentum. What is the pattern of this particular kind of activation sequence?

Here again we have no right to assume that there must be only one pattern. We can sometimes draw diagrams of the actual processes of activation, and even take photographs of its operation. The patterns that have already been found are various. The well-known photographs of flashes of lightning taken at night show wavering lines, dividing and sub-dividing; rather like a map of a river and its tributaries, but upside down, beginning with the estuary and ending with the sources. Diagrams of the lines of force, as physicists call them, round the poles of a magnet, disclosed by the way fine iron filings on a sheet of paper arrange themselves when brought within the magnetic field, consist of groups of curves centered on the poles. Another diagram of the lines of force within an electrometer shows them somewhat resembling plumes or brushes of feathers, side by side in rows. We might perhaps plausibly picture the pattern, in the cases of momentum that have been given in illustration, as like a rod; with a cross-section corresponding more or less with that of the stone, the billiard-ball, the wagon or the train. Such a rod-like sequence might not have definite edges. Its influence would probably be felt as a blur in the adjacent quiescent ether, perhaps giving rise to lateral waves or 'wavelets.'

A rod-like pattern of activation in the initiating force would account for an object being projected along the same straight line by the continuing force, as posited in Newton's First Law of Motion.

3

Not only the shape, but the velocity of such a motor-activation would appear to depend on that of the initiating factor. In the case of momentum, velocity is evidently not uniform and specific to the medium, as in radiation and gravitation. It may be as slow as the movement of a billiard-ball sent gently across the table; or as fast as a railway-train, or a bullet in flight, or again a planet in its orbit.

The duration of a motor-activation sequence may also vary indefinitely—from a moment to perpetuity. It depends upon the resultant of the velocity of the initiating movement and the mass of the object, together with any forces afterwards "impressed upon it." The process may be ended altogether by an effective obstruction.

The originating impact may be either sudden or gradual. In the latter case it is cumulative, and takes time to produce its effect; as with the horses straining at the wagon, or the athlete whirling the hammer. Often the initiating movement, caused by an outside agent—a man, or an engine, or perhaps the explosion of gases in a cartridge—will overlap for a short time with the continuing movement caused by the ether activation: the transition will then be gradual from one to the other. We say that during that time the object "is gathering momentum."

Mathematically, momentum is the product of mass multiplied by velocity. The greater these are at the outset the stronger will be the impact and the bigger the resulting momentum: witness the difference in speed between a game of squash rackets played with a soft rubber ball and a game of court-tennis with a heavier hard ball. (All ball games and all athletics are tests of skill or of strength in establishing impetus, in various ways and in various degrees. A pedant might describe them as exercises in the art of ether-activation.)

If a particular combination of mass and velocity is not above the minimum necessary in all cases for activation, it will prove abortive. Every continuing motion has had its initiating cause, but not every would-be initiative succeeds in establishing a continuation.

GRAVITATION (II) 1

We will now revert to the crucial problem of gravitation.

We have seen that there are strong grounds for believing that a mechanism of waves, radiated from a gravitational center and of the general order of the known electromagnetic wave-system, forms part of the gravitational process; and that this hypothesis has been formulated by Einstein and Eddington and is now generally accepted by physicists.[3] Assuming then, that they exist, let us first consider what the nature of these gravital waves is likely to be.

The classes of waves belonging to different parts of the wave-band produce, we know, effects that are very different from one another: it would not be remarkable that the gravital waves should have qualities different from all the rest. It is evident that this is so, especially in respect of penetrating power. Light, x-rays, and gamma-rays have different, and limited, powers of penetration. Gravity penetrates everything.

But it will be obvious that this outward radiation of gravitational influence cannot be the whole of the process

[3] Einstein, in a new Appendix to the fourth edition, published in 1950, of his book *The Meaning of Relativity,* presents a series of equations reconciling gravitation with electromagnetic radiation. But it is noteworthy that he prefaces the statement by saying: "In the following I shall present an attempt at the solution of this problem which appears to me highly convincing although, due to mathematical difficulties, I have not yet found a practicable way to confront the results of the theory with experimental evidence."

that we are examining. It does not account, first, for outlying objects being set in motion; and secondly for the movement not being in the direction of the outgoing waves, but the reverse. Since this movement and its direction are an essential part of the situation—are given facts—they must be accounted for, if at all, by something other than this outward radiation from the center.

2

The proposition that I would offer for consideration is that *Gravitation is not a single process but dual: a combination of two distinct processes, separable in location and different in kind.*

In what follows I shall discuss the attraction—as we are accustomed to call it—of a gravitational center for some relatively small outlying object within its field. For the sake of conciseness I will call the first the 'center' and the second the 'object.' There is, of course, a reciprocal attraction of the smaller object for the larger center; but this can be considered separately. And as in our practical experience this reciprocal attraction is usually insignificant—for example a ball dropping to the earth is also drawing the earth up to itself, but only in a degree inversely proportionate to their relative masses—we usually leave it out of account, except when some special occasion arises for including it. I shall do the same here.

We conceive, then, that a center is continuously radiating spherical ether-waves of great penetrating power, able to transpierce all forms of matter. In their course, a pencil of such waves meets with an object, and passes through it. But it appears that, as a consequence of its passage, a second ether process is set up, in and around the object, which puts it in motion. This motion is in the opposite direction—backwards towards the center.

The movement of bodies under the influence of gravity has therefore the same duality in causation as all the other forms of motion that we have been discussing. There is first an initiating impact, and secondly what we may term a motor-activation of the ether, localized where the object is. In those other cases, however, the initiating movement has not been a simple ether-activation: it has been the movement of a hand, of horses, or a railway-engine, or the like. In the case of gravity the initiating cause has been itself an ether-activation, but of a different kind from the first, and producing quite different phenomena. The first is of the spherical wave pattern; the second is not, but is of the motor pattern, whatever that may be. The first has the uniform velocity of all radiation, that of light; the second has velocities much smaller and varying. The first is propagated outward from the center; the second moves, or tends to move, towards the center. It is not the case, as is usually supposed, that the center is active and the object passive (apart from its own reciprocal power of attraction). Both are active agents; each takes part independently in the process as a whole.

Between the place where the center is and the place where the object is, lies the ether, which transmits first the radiant-activation from the center to the object and afterwards the motor-activation from the object towards the center. It supplies the factor of contiguity, without which neither could affect the other in any way at all.

3

Before dealing with the many questions that at once present themselves as to the possibility and the working of such a system, I would offer some illustrations, drawn from our daily environment, which may help us to picture it.

1. Broadcasting is a fairly close analogy. It exhibits a dual process that is similar in principle. The initiation comes from a radio station which is continuously emitting Hertzian waves; the ether transmits them in all directions. When a receiving-set is present within range, a fresh and different process of activation is started. It is not a radiation, but is of a motor type; the velocity it develops is not that of light, but much slower; the power that actuates the set—causing the diaphragm of the loud-speaker to vibrate and send out sound-waves into the air—is not the power which is working the distant broadcasting station, but is supplied, on the spot, by a battery attached to the set or from the power-house serving the district.

2. I have a wooden ball in my hand and toss it across the room to a child. In the terminology we are using we would say that, between my hand and the child, the ball has been pushed—or wafted—through the air by a motor-activation of the ether in and around the ball; the child feels its effect when he catches the ball and stops it.

Now I place the ball on the table near the edge. We say that the ball is at rest and passive. A touch rolls it past the edge, and instantly it is swept down to the floor. The motor-activation which carries it perpendicularly to the floor is precisely of the same order as that which had previously carried it horizontally across the room. The first movement was initiated by an impact from a motion of my arm. How has the second been initiated?

Not by anything fresh that happened at the moment when the ball was pushed over the edge of the table. All the time that it had been resting there it had 'weight,' which was pressing it down on the table; it did not carry it to the floor only because the table was in the way. While apparently at rest, something dynamic was going on in and about the ball. The instant the ball was free of the table it was swept downward.

3. Another illustration of a similar kind can prove that this is so by the direct evidence of our senses. Suppose that I have some heavy object, say a large bronze clock, standing on a marble mantelpiece. I wish to move it; and, succeeding by an effort in tilting it a little with one hand, I insert the fingers of the other under the base; only to find that the clock is too heavy to lift and that I cannot disengage my fingers. Until I can release myself, or get someone to come and help me, my fingers are being painfully pinched.

It is beyond question that whatever physical process was going on during those seconds or minutes, in and about the clock and the mantelpiece, had been going on before and will be going on after: it did not begin when I put my fingers there, or end when I got them away. We had regarded the clock as being static; and that was true, in the sense that it was not in motion relatively to its surroundings. But we can now realize that something highly dynamic, invisible and of which we had been unaware, had been, is and will be, going on there incessantly.

We might say that everyone knows the cause of all this to be simply the pressure of the weight of the clock on the mantelpiece. But the words Pressure and Weight merely indicate what the problem is: they do not point to any solution. Nor is it solved by saying that it arises from the inward pull of the earth's gravity; for, if our authorities are right, what the earth does in the matter is to emit a continuous series of electromagnetic waves outwards. To account for the weight and the pressure there must be some kind of reverse activity, and the proposition is that this can only emanate in and about the clock itself.

4. For my last illustration I revert to the question of the tides.

This is a case of the reciprocal attraction of the smaller object for the larger. On the one hand the earth sends out gravital waves which evoke in the moon a motor-activation in reverse. On the other hand the moon sends out its own gravital waves which have a similar effect on the earth. The earth consequently tends to move towards the moon; it does not do so on account of its momentum in its orbit. But the oceans, being fluid and not consolidated with the mass of the globe, are to some extent free to move. They are thus the theatre of two forces, in the ether in and about them, which are working opposite ways. One is a local motor-force evoked by the earth's gravital waves, which pushes the molecules of water downwards: the other is a local motor-force evoked by the moon's gravital waves, which pushes the molecules upwards. The movement of the tides is the resultant of the two. (The effect of the sun's gravity has not been taken into account.) The conclusion is that the immediate cause of a rising tide is not, as it appears, a pull or suction from the distant energy of the moon, but a push here by the present energy of the earth.

4

Various questions and criticisms spring into our minds when we begin to consider a proposition such as this. In the first place, what kind of mechanism can we suppose it to be which produces the movement of a material object in one direction as a consequence of an electromagnetic radiation in the opposite direction?

We can only answer that we do not know. But we can add that we are equally ignorant of the way in which all the other transformations that we find in nature are brought about, phenomena with which we are familiar every day and every hour.

Review, for example, the changes which energy undergoes between the furnaces of a power-house and an electric lamp in a room. Coal is burned and produces molecular heat; the heat evaporates water in the boilers; the expansion of the steam (to 1400 times the liquid volume) causes motion in the turbines or piston-rods of the engines; the motion gives rise to magnetism in the generators and sends currents of electrons travelling along wires; the electric current does mechanical work in factories, produces light in lamps or radiant heat in electric stoves. What is the actual event that happens at the point where any one of these processes changes into one of the others? We do not know.

Newton, discussing "the changing of Bodies into Light, and Light into Bodies," says that "it is very conformable to the Course of Nature, which seems delighted with Transmutations." The ingenuity of man uses them; they have been made, indeed, the material bases of our present civilization. The engineer evolves this sequence of heat, gaseous expansion, motion, magnetism, electric current, light—or else heat again, or mechanical work; but all the time he does not understand how the transformations he is manipulating have been effected. Gravitation adds yet another to these, for us, secret and mysterious processes. It is not surprising that we cannot explain its mechanism. If gravity were explicable while all the others were not—it is that which would be surprising.

This inability on our part cannot in any degree affect the reality of the metamorphoses. With gravity as with the others, the proof of an underlying process of transformation is given by empirical experience. The whole universe bears witness. Wherever there is matter, mass, weight—a ball dropping to the floor, a clock pressing continuously on the mantelpiece, a tide creeping up the beach—some combination of a gravital radiation with a motor response is made manifest.

5

We are supposing that a stream of highly penetrating gravital waves, rushing through a material object with the velocity of light, by its passage sets up an independent stream of activation, of a different kind, in the ether situated there: it is this which sets the object moving (if it is free to move) in the opposite direction. A second question is whether this will involve a diminution in the strength of the outward radiation.

If it does, the force of gravity will be lessened by the obstruction of a substantial object. If it does not, then the law of the conservation of energy is being infringed. But neither of these postulates would at present be admitted by physicists. If energy is spent on this 'backward kick,' as it may be described, observation ought to be able to detect the loss: no evidence, however, has ever been forthcoming. If no energy is lost, then, it is said, such a phenomenon could not happen at all, the law of conservation is absolute and would forbid it.

On this, several possibilities may be conceived.

(*a*) Some gravital energy—I use this term for convenience instead of saying, more precisely, "strength of the activation of the ether by gravital radiation"—may in fact be lost on the passage, but its amount may be too small to be detected. For instance, in the case of the earth and any object on or near its surface, the first factor in the process is a radiation of tremendous power and enormous velocity. Although continuously diminished by diffusion, in the ratio of the square of the distance travelled, it is strong enough to continue its activating impact as far out into the universe as the earth's gravitational influence can be felt: on or near the earth's surface its strength is at the maximum. The second factor is the energy, activated in and about the object, which pushes it down towards the earth. The mass of the object is infinitesimally minute relatively to that of the earth which is generating the outward waves. The speed of the downward motion is only of the order usual in terrestrial conditions. It is therefore evident that the two factors are completely out of scale with one another.

Even if we were to take the sun as center and the earth as object and were to suppose that the sun's gravital influence was being reduced in some degree by its transit through the earth, the degree could only be exceedingly small. The waves will be travelling for millions, or tens of millions of light-years: their passage through the center of the earth would be a matter of eight thousand miles, or about a twenty-fifth of a second. It is unlikely that the most delicate tests, even if any tests were practicable, could detect the loss.

(*b*) It is possible that, supposing such loss, it might be counteracted, or concealed, by some process akin to that of the diffraction of light.

Grimsehl's *Textbook of Physics* says that "when light-waves, or any wave motion, encounters a medium with different properties, the waves partly are reflected and partly enter the medium and are refracted. . . . The non-reflected part of the light enters the body and either passes through it or is absorbed in it, *i.e.*, its energy is changed into another form, usually into heat." There is no reason to suppose that gravital energy is reflected by objects; nor need any question of absorption arise. Almost the whole of the energy passes through, but there appears to be no reason for rejecting a possibility that a small part may be refracted, or else diffracted.

Diffraction, says Grimsehl, is "the capacity of waves for passing round an obstacle and reinforcing one another in the rear of the obstacle by superposition." . . . In a beam of light, "at a sufficient distance behind a small obstacle there is no longer a proper shadow (when parallel light is used)." If a similar principle applies in another part of the electromagnetic wave-band—in gravitation, we may envisage the gravital waves, in their passage through matter, encountering a series of small obstacles, perhaps atoms, or perhaps the particles constituting the atoms. If that is so, this process, of the waves dividing and then rejoining after the obstacle has been passed, might apply here. Indeed since gravital waves are evidently far more powerful and insistent than light waves, the process may be more complete, and the 'shadow' might be eliminated altogether. In that case the effect might be as though their original force remained unimpaired. And this might conceivably account for the fact—as it is now considered to be—that it is impossible to 'screen off' the force of gravity.

(*c*) A third possibility remains. The 'backward kick' may in fact require an expenditure of some of the energy of the outward gravital waves. This might indeed come to be established mathematically. And good reason might be shown for rejecting any speculation that this could be made good or explained away by supposing a process of diffraction, or in any other way. Still it need not follow that the whole conception must be abandoned because the conclusion could not be escaped that it contradicts the principle of the conservation of energy. The alternative remains that the principle itself may not hold, in the form now accepted, when we are dealing with certain of the phenomena produced by a Two-State Ether. This is a point we have hitherto reserved, and we must still reserve it until we come to consider, a little more closely than is yet possible, the idea of quiescent energy itself.

6

Another question that arises is how, on these principles, can we account for the fact that the velocity of a falling object is continually being accelerated? We have said that the cause of the movement of a dropped ball is essentially the same as that of a thrown ball—an initiating stimulus giving rise to a continuing ether-activation. If that is so, why are not both subject to the same acceleration; or else neither?

This question does not present the same difficulty as the previous ones. For it is evident that the difference in the two cases is due to the difference in the character of the initiating cause. With the thrown ball it is the movement of my hand: this operates once for all: the moment my hand releases the ball its function is over: the ball then travels at uniform speed in a straight line, in accordance with Newton's First Law, unless and until other forces intervene. With the dropped ball it is otherwise. The original propelling factor is followed and reinforced by a series of others; and these are stronger and stronger the nearer the object draws towards the gravitational center. The effect is to increase its velocity.

Let the imagination watch the event as it is happening. Suppose an object being dropped from a balloon, floating say a thousand feet above the ground. Before it is dropped, while resting in the car of the balloon, upward gravital waves from the earth are passing through it, and evoking, by their passage, in the ether there present, a downward motor-push. This would carry the object down if it were free to move: it does so the moment the object is dropped over the side. The strength of the upward waves has depended upon the distance they had travelled, in accordance with the inverse-square rule. The strength of the downward push will vary with the strength of the waves which had evoked it. Consequently the velocity of the object, as it leaves the balloon, is related to the strength of the earth's gravitational influence at that height—a thousand feet. Now as it travels down, the object meets a continual succession of ascending waves, and the strength of these is greater and greater as the distance they have travelled from the earth's surface, where it was at the maximum, becomes less and less. The effect is cumulative. By the time the object reaches five hundred feet its impetus —that is, the push of the ether action which is carrying it —is much greater than when it started; and when it hits the ground it does so with a velocity that is relatively high. The blow that it strikes is many times greater than if a precisely similar object were dropped from a window, say ten feet above the ground.

A light object and a heavy object fall with the same velocity, and will arrive at the same time, because both are moved by energy which is activated in an equal degree, on parallel lines, by the same causes. It is like a log of wood and a cork set afloat on a river reaching a given point at the same time. It is the current which determines the time, not the character of the objects which happen to be floating in it.

7

Students of science will share the surprise expressed by Sir Edmund Whittaker that gravitation, although one of the first problems to be attacked by physics, still remains perplexing. Our last question will be to ask whether any explanation can be offered for this failure to discover the mechanism of the most universal of all natural phenomena.

Several observations may be offered.

(*a*) The very universality of gravity keeps it unknown. It pervades everything and passes through everything. It cannot be revealed by the senses, because the sense organs are already saturated with it. It gives no hold for scientific observation and experiment, because no vessel can contain it, no apparatus measure it, no lens deflect it or prism dissect. Gravital radiation is universal and incessant in and around us, and we are unaware that it exists just for that reason. Would deep-sea fishes be aware that they live in water?

(*b*) Imperceptible by the senses, only the intellect can discover it, through its effects. And the intellect is continually defeating its own efforts by imposing on them unnecessary conditions. In particular, there is the constant, irrational tendency to insist upon seeking a single cause for a class of events or phenomena, when the truth may be that there is a combination of two causes, or more.

For example, it was not possible to account for the phases of the moon when it was assumed to be a luminary, shining spontaneously, of the same order as the sun: God had created "the greater light to rule the day and the lesser light to rule the night." Everything became simple when it was realized that moonlight had a double origin: the sun emitted the light and the moon merely reflected that part which fell upon it. Momentum is another example: so long as it is assumed that motion is a single process, due to a single cause, it remains inexplicable. If it is seen to be a process always in two phases—separate, different, and consecutive—the one initiating, the other continuing, the problem will be well on the way to solution.

Of this readiness to be misled by appearance, of this constant obsession by causal unity, gravitation, we suggest, is yet another instance. We observe a gravitational center and an outlying object and we see that the one 'attracts' the other. It is assumed that the center is active and the object is passive (except in so far as it acts itself as a center and 'attracts' the other reciprocally). It is supposed that the process must consist essentially of a 'pull' by the center upon the object, which itself does no more than respond and obey. But this term Attraction is a misnomer. It may be useful as a compendious name to describe the situation as a whole. When we analyse it we find that the word is altogether misleading. Two activities are engaged and not one. There is no pull at all. The center radiates outwards, and then the object is pushed inwards by the ether located where it is. In addition, the ether in between is a factor which sustains both streams of activation. We create our own perplexity by tacitly assuming a unity that in fact does not exist.

(*c*) But in any case it was most unlikely that at any time before the present century science was ready to come to close quarters with this inner mystery. So long as atoms —and therefore material objects—were regarded as static entities, endowed by nature with solidity and weight as inherent qualities, it was hardly possible for physics to get very far. Only when the discoveries of J. J. Thomson and Rutherford had shown that matter was not static, that all its manifestations were caused by dynamic processes, only then was the way open for a theory that gravity was of the same order.

(*d*) If this is accepted, and if the line of inquiry suggested in this essay were considered worth pursuing further, our search would be narrowed down to the single point—how can an ether-wave movement, when it impinges on matter, elicit an inverse motor-activation?

We know of several cases in nature where a movement, proceeding in one direction, is reversed or turned aside on meeting some material obstacle. A universal example is the reflection, refraction, or diffraction of light. Familiar also is the echo: a sequence of sound waves in the air, striking a cliff or wall, is sent back towards its point of origin. Radar furnishes a modern instance. Another is the reflection of broadcasting waves by the Heaviside, Appleton, and other layers of the ionosphere; although here the obstacle is not material but a difference in the state of the medium which the waves have encountered.

All these, however, are cases in which the same waves are redirected, or one set of waves is stopped and absorbed and another set, of the same kind and with the same velocity, is set going in the opposite, or some other direction. On the principle here suggested, the case of gravitation would be different from any of these. Not only would the direction be exactly reversed, but a spherical radiation would evoke some kind of motor-activation of another pattern and with a quite different velocity. It may well be that this process is unique. That it should be so is no reason for denying its actuality. Others of the transformations which, for empirical reasons, we accept as fact, may also each be unique. That the innermost mechanism of gravity has not yet been discovered, and that it may prove to be unique, are not reasons for asserting that there can be no mechanism of the nature suggested.[4]

[4] I regret that, when writing this paragraph for the original edition of this book, I did not cite the phenomena of magnetism as probably a valid example of the kind of double process that has been suggested for gravitation. Consider, for instance, an electric crane in a modern iron foundry. A large magnet is suspended by a strong chain from a carriage travelling along a gantry under the roof: it is brought to a spot near the entrance of the foundry where a heap of scrap-iron has been dumped, and is lowered to a point close above the heap. The moment that the current of electricity from the main supply is switched on and the magnet is activated, the nearest pieces of iron rise to the magnet and cling to it, and those below cling to the first, the whole forming a cohesive cluster. The crane then transports the magnet with its adhesions to another part of the foundry, close to the furnaces where the metal is to be melted; then the current is switched off, and instantly the whole cluster ceases to adhere and drops to the ground. Here we have—first, an outward current passing from the magnet in a wave forma-

We may sometimes be tempted to say that man will never be able to solve these mysteries. The maxim is a good one—"Never use the word never."

8

These conclusions on Gravitation have a bearing upon the question of Momentum, discussed in earlier sections (pages 46, 71, 101). When speaking of the problems that are still outstanding I asked, "Why should a ball that has been thrown continue, after it has been released from the hand, to travel indefinitely in a straight line away from the thrower . . .?" One of the physicists who kindly read the earlier drafts of this essay countered this by asking, "Why shouldn't it?" I find that others are ready to do the same; and, assuming that the second question is unanswerable, are content to put the first aside and pass on. I must therefore return to the point in order to take up the challenge—"Why shouldn't it?"

I assume that no one will deny that gravity is to be accepted as empirical fact—any material object, on or

tion; secondly, a quite different process evoked within, and probably around, each individual piece of iron near enough to be affected, which operates in the opposite direction. And this is not merely a reflection of the current, since its effect is different, being a molar movement, lifting up the pieces of iron to touch the magnet, or to touch the overlying pieces of iron that are in immediate contact with it. The whole can then be raised, countering the attraction of the earth's gravity, but yielding to gravity again the moment that the electric current is discontinued. Are we not witnessing before our eyes the exact process which has been suggested as that of gravity—an outward wave radiation eliciting as response an inward molar movement?

near the earth's surface, whether at rest or in motion, is continuously being drawn (or pushed) towards the earth's center, and, if free, will move towards it. And probably no one will dispute that the movement of the thrown ball across the room is also empirical fact. Although the ball is a passive object, with no motive-power of its own, we can watch it flying through the air, foot by foot, making its way through the real, though invisible, atoms and molecules of the air that impede it, and, if thrown hard enough, striking the opposite wall with violence. If some perverse philosopher is still not satisfied of the 'reality' of the motion as an event in the perceived universe, I could get someone to take a photograph, with a slow exposure, at the moment the ball is thrown: the movement, relative to the camera and to the room, will be shown as a line across the picture: unless the event had 'really' happened that line could not be there.

It will be agreed too that while the ball is at rest on the table it does not fall to the floor, under the influence of gravity, for a definite reason, namely the interposition of the table; and that it does not fall to the floor while it is being held in my hand, whether at rest or during the act of throwing, for a similar reason—the interposition of the bones and muscles of my body.

We know that the ball, if it were to be gently pushed over the edge of the table, or merely released by my hand, would instantly fall perpendicularly to the floor; but that, when thrown, it does not do that, but something quite different—it travels almost horizontally across the room. It is not enough therefore to meet the situation by saying that no reason need be given for the horizontal movement.

A reason has been given for a perpendicular movement—the gravitational influence of the earth. If that movement does not at once take place, something must be preventing it—and this is no longer the obstruction of a material body, such as a table or a hand.

Nor is it enough to say that the something that is upholding the ball during its transit, and preventing it from falling instantly to the ground, is its 'velocity,' or 'momentum,' or 'impetus.' Velocity is a measurement; it is a concomitant of a movement already taking place; it is coincident with the movement and not prior to it; it can therefore have no operative effect of any kind. Momentum or Impetus are also words which *describe* what is happening; they do not *account for* it. To say that they do is sheer scholasticism; it is an attempt to treat linguistic terms as though they could be factors in a sequence of physical events. A theory that it is the possession—whatever Possession may mean—of velocity, or momentum, or impetus, which prevents the thrown ball from immediately falling to the floor, cannot satisfy.

Consider, further, this circumstance, which will not be challenged as empirical fact. If there is no wall in the way, the thrown ball will gradually descend to the floor along the line of a parabolic curve. This curve can be ascertained, or predicted, mathematically, as the resultant of two forces—gravity acting perpendicularly, and some other acting horizontally. But unless this other is of the same order of reality as gravity, the two could not act upon each other as they do, to some extent countering each other, and producing a course for the ball which is not a straight line, either perpendicular or horizontal, but a curve in between. Of the two forces, gravity is physically real: we watch the phenomena it produces at every moment. Can we then avoid the conclusion that the other—the force acting horizontally—must also be physically real, and not something that is merely mathematical or linguistic?

An analogy may be seen in Einstein's discovery that gravitation and light radiation can interact; confirmed by astronomical observations during eclipses of the sun that the light from a distant star is deflected when passing near a powerful gravitational center. From this it must follow that gravitation and light radiation are processes, not the same, but of the same order of reality, and transmitted by the same medium. It is therefore not difficult to conceive that the gravity which pulls an object downward, and the force, whatever it is, which is carrying it forward, are of the same order; operating in the same medium and interacting with one another; so causing the object to follow a course that is neither the one straight line nor the other, but a curve which is the resultant of the two.

Let us then fix our minds on the moment after the ball has left the hand; when it does not drop perpendicularly downward, as it would do if simply released, but instead travels almost horizontally onwards—for this is the essence of the whole matter. Here is indeed the critical point at issue in present-day theoretical physics.

It is evident that the event that takes place is consequent upon the co-ordinated movement of the arm and hand which constitutes the act of throwing, because nothing else has happened that would account for the event, while this would account for it. But the ball's transit across the room *is consequent upon* the act of throwing, and not directly and immediately caused by it, because the arm and hand are now no longer in actual contact with the ball; the muscular effort is over and done with; it is an event in the past, not in the present, whereas the ball is travelling on now, in the present. The conclusion is that there must be some physical factor—not the air, as we know—which is operating to cause this. It would seem that only if this is definitely admitted, once for all, shall we be able to approach, with any hope of success, the problem of Momentum.

I would put the same point another way with the help of a different example. Consider a truck being shunted on a railway siding. The shunting engine pushes it a certain distance and then stops, and the truck travels forward, as we say, "by its own impetus." Apart from air resistance, or being stopped by other trucks on the line or by buffers, it will not go on indefinitely, but gradually come to a standstill. We are told that this is due to "the force of friction." But what is the cause of the friction? It is the pressure of the framework of the truck upon the axles of the wheels. And why is there any pressure? Because of the weight of the truck. But weight is nothing but a manifestation of gravity. It is therefore the known force of gravity which, sooner or later, brings the truck to a standstill. When we ask why it is that it does not instantly come to a standstill as soon as the engine stops pushing, it is evidently no answer to ask, "Why should it?" because the reply is obvious: it would, like the ball, be stopped by gravity—unless some force, capable of interacting with gravity and countering it, were present and active.

One of my consultants wrote, with regard to the similar illustration of the train being started by the pull of the engine (see page 82) that "it is not the downward pull of gravity, but the inertia of the mass of the train, that is overcome." But when I ask what is Inertia and what is Mass, I get no answer, except in other terms of a mathematical nature. Gravity is factual, as we realize every time we drop an object or tread upon the ground. Radiation is factual, as we realize every time we see something or turn on our radio set. Energy is also factual, as we see in the flash of lightning or in the explosion of an atom bomb. We may trace back radiation—and it now seems gravitation also—to the oscillation of atoms; and the atoms themselves are factual, as we find in chemistry and in nuclear physics. But the others—Momentum, Mass, Inertia—and also Force—these, like Space and Time, are not factual but fictional. We may ring the changes on these concepts and show how they all sustain one another; and if, in any instance, they are found not to do so, all that is necessary is to re-define the assumptions that we have ourselves invented as the basis for those concepts. But if we persist in asking what is actually happening in the universe to keep a train stationary until an engine starts pulling it; or to bring a shunted truck to a standstill; or to carry a thrown ball across a room—to refer us to these fictional abstractions does not satisfy. They may justify one another in their own mathematical world, which is part of human thought, but they can *do* nothing in the phenomenal universe.

Another of my physicist friends, to whom I put in conversation the need for an explanation why a thrown ball should continue to travel after it had been released from the hand, replied, "But how about motion in free space?" My answer was that I am not now dealing with free space; that is a separate matter, to be considered in relation to its own conditions. I am dealing with terrestrial conditions, with the empirical facts around us, including gravity: and it is legitimate to do that, for the conditions in which we carry on our lives—including discussions such as these—are as much a part of the factual universe as are those of free space.

9

I conclude by submitting, with respect, that this argument should be either rebutted or accepted. It is not to be evaded by saying that the thrown ball, or the shunted truck, continues to move when the propelling force is withdrawn "because that is what it does"; or, as Whitehead puts it, "because that is its natural motion"; and that there is no need to say anything more about it. There is a need, because a known physical force is acting all the time to prevent or stop the horizontal movement; and unless some other equivalent force, at present unidentified, is also operating to sustain it along its initial line of motion, the phenomena, which we have accepted as facts, could not take place.

The suggestion that is offered here is, therefore, that the existence of this unidentified physical factor must be regarded—not as an arbitrary assumption, invented in order to serve a logical purpose and to be accepted or rejected as we like—but as a direct inference from observed facts.

The further proposition is advanced that this force, now unrecognized, may be identified with a constituent of the universe—energy—which is already known to us; is indeed nowadays very familiar, since we are using it every day for our own purposes—as freely as we use stones and trees, or the water of the rivers or the wind over the sea.

Here as I write, in London, in my library, I have around me no fewer than eight examples of this—a telephone, a radio set, electric lamps, an electric heater, an electric bell, power connection for a vacuum cleaner, two old-fashioned mirrors set in the wall, and windows which let in the daylight but shut out the wind, the rain and the cold. To these I might add my own brain and nervous system, which comprise an electric installation far more elaborate than any of the others. Also the earth's gravity, which holds me and my table and all the objects around me to the floor, and the room itself and the house to the ground. Likewise the rotation of the globe, which gives me day and night; and its momentum in its orbit, upholding it at a comfortable distance from the sun—not too near and not too far. Every one of these is a visible, tangible proof of the existence of an ether as an underlying component of the universe—not to be wiped out and ignored on the plea that, at the present moment in human history, mathematical physicists have been unable, or unwilling, to find a place for it in their cosmic equations.

Why then should we seek for something new and unknown to account for the phenomena that we observe, until we have first considered whether something that is so well-known as Energy may not account for them quite satisfactorily?

To this is added a speculation that the mechanism of such a system might be understandable if this energy exists in either of two states—of inertia or of activity, and that these phenomena all result from transitions between them. Further that this principle might give a clue, not only to the problem of the cause of momentum, but also to the problems of the nature of gravity, of the transmission both of gravity and of radiation, and of the appearance and disappearance of particles and their movement.

Such notions may be right or wrong. If they are wrong, let the errors be pointed out and no more will be heard of them. But then let some alternative be sought for. If, on the other hand, there is a possibility that they or some parts of them, may be right, then to explore them further would be well worth while.

All this is clearly the business of the theoretical physicists; not of philosophers, who can only be expected to deal with these matters in an amateurish way—as in this essay. Apparently, however, the physicists of the present day refuse to adopt any of the three courses—to accept, to reject, or to inquire.

But this is to desert what has been regarded hitherto by modern science as its fundamental duty. Had this agnostic principle prevailed five centuries ago and since, the discoveries of Copernicus, Galileo, Boyle, Dalton, Faraday, the Curies, Einstein, and J. J. Thomson and Rutherford would never have been achieved; their explorations would not even have been attempted. In each of these great problems, momentous to human thought, we are now, as I have said, at a dead-end. For the physicists to be content to leave us there would be to abandon that tradition of eager and indomitable inquiry which has made possible the illustrious contributions of science to the progress of civilization; which has been indeed the prime origin of the great sequence of splendid achievements, intellectual and practical, that have won the admiration and the gratitude of mankind.

V. Quiescent Energy

1

Before concluding this essay we must consider more closely the conception of quiescent energy. In doing so we shall be able to pick up some threads, left loose in the course of the argument, relating to the bearing of a scheme such as this on the Law of the Conservation of Energy, as now generally understood and accepted.

First let me recapitulate the principal points that have been put forward, with some expansions.

Quiescence is inertial, but inertia is not nothingness: quiescent energy is physically real.

It exists without phenomena: the moment there are phenomena, there is no longer quiescence.

The Two-State Ether is observable, and can be described, when it is in the active state; our accounts of the universe that we perceive are its description. When it is in the quiescent, or inertial, state it is unobservable and indescribable. But it is not, for that reason, non-existent.

The function of quiescent energy is twofold: it is the matrix from which active energy emerges, and it is the inertia into which active energy may relapse.

Active energy is in patterns of various types: (1) radiating waves: studied for nearly three hundred years; (2) particles: recognized and identified only since the end of the nineteenth century; (3) apparently also what we have termed here 'motor-activation,' causing the movement of substantial (or molar) objects; this has not yet been identified and studied.

Gravitation may be the effect of a combination of the first with the third.

It is, of course, conceivable that there are other activity-patterns of which we are not aware and may perhaps have no means of becoming aware.

Any pattern must be a pattern of something other than itself. There could be no patterns of ether-activity unless there had already been something prior, which they could be patterns of. Active-ether patterns produce phenomena that are physically real—all the phenomena of the known universe. This is why quiescent energy—which is the prior state from which activity emerges, and which it patterns—must be equally real.

Quiescent energy makes possible the transmission of light and other radiations, and the movement of objects. It also makes possible the emergence of particles, and therefore of matter in general. None of these would be possible in empty space.

2

The ether taken as a whole—quiescent and active together—is universal and continuous: nothing exists anywhere that can be an alternative. There can be no question, therefore, of increasing or diminishing, conserving or destroying it. (Unless indeed the entire universe that we perceive can be localized in relation to something physical which is not itself. As to this we know nothing.)

Active energy, taken separately, is not universal and continuous. It is differentiated, first from quiescent energy, and afterwards into its own various patterns. Questions therefore arise whether or not the amount of energy that is in the active state must remain constant, either in some manifestation at a particular time and place, or in its total in the universe as a whole.

It has been found empirically that whenever active energy is changed from one form to another—heat, mechanical work, electric current, light, and so forth—through all metamorphoses the energy remains the same in amount. The engineer can measure it at every stage; he can account for any loss incidental to the working of the mechanisms; he finds that the total is always unchanged. This law of the conservation of energy has been proved by universal experience to apply to all such transformations; and this is not open to challenge.

It has, however, been assumed to follow from this that any other kind of energy change must be subject to the same law. Physicists generally are not prepared to give consideration to any new ether hypothesis unless the condition is first satisfied that it will not be inconsistent with the law of conservation. For this *a priori* condition I have not yet seen any reason advanced. It seems, indeed, that it is not thought necessary to advance reasons. Universal experience having shown that, wherever our observation extends, the law of conservation holds, we are to infer that whenever we pass beyond the range of observation it will still hold. But, valuable as the method of inference is, we have to be sure in any particular case that the conditions are substantially the same. That is not so here.

We are now considering the transitions in a Two-State Ether from one state to the other. This is a wholly different process from all those which have formed the basis for the principle of conservation. Because those shiftings of the frequencies of radiations, or conversions into molar motion, or into currents of electrons, or the like, are effected without change in the amount of the activity engaged, that is no reason for saying that the total amount of activity anywhere in the universe must always remain the same. Nor even that every particular activity, at a given place and time, must continue unchanged in amount, indefinitely.

We picture an ocean of energy in a state generally of quiescence, but with waves of radiation constantly flickering in it; and numberless particles forming, and either enduring or dissolving. A part of this ether which is in the active state at one instant may have relapsed into quiescence at the next. We cannot expect to know whether the amount of activity—either in some localized part, or in its universal total—is constant, or is diminishing, or is increasing. It does not appear indeed, that even if an answer to that question were possible, it would have any special significance, for science or for philosophy. But however that may be, we certainly have no right to assume as an axiom that the amount must be constant. To insist that the whole science of physics must be forced into that framework would merely be to subject it, quite gratuitously, to crippling disabilities.

We have given reasons for thinking that, if there is such an ether, the transition from quiescence to action must have a threshold, that there is a specific minimum. If so, a particular stream of activation may later fall back below that minimum. Then the process must end. This may come about, in the case of radiation, through diffusion, since the strength of the wave-impulse is always diminishing in accordance with the inverse-square law. It may also come about through the intervention of other forces —the obstruction of a gas, as with air friction, or the resistance of a massive object. The stream of activation will then cease; it will subside into inertia, as the ripples on a pond disappear and the water is smooth again; or as the radio waves from a broadcasting station fade away, sooner or later according to the amount of power it generates.

Depending upon the circumstances of the case, a particular activation may extend over any distance, from an infinitesimal fraction of a millimetre to astronomical dimensions; and may endure for any period, from an instant to perpetuity.

The difference, then, between the conservation theory at present accepted and the scheme now proposed, is this. Under the first, it is held that energy cannot disappear; it can only be changed from one form into another. Under the second, energy, as such, also cannot disappear; but any given activation may cease and lapse into inertia. When that happens we have no means of tracing it further. Nor would we have any reason for wishing to do so.

3

If the general scheme submitted here were found acceptable, it would continue to sustain the great mathematical systems of Clerk Maxwell, of relativity theory, of quantum mechanics, and of electronics generally. The functions assigned by them to an electromagnetic 'field' would be fulfilled by the ether. The attribution of physical qualities to a mental concept, as with the spacetime continuum, not being admitted, the ether, which is claimed to be physically real, would be the substitute. It would furnish a material basis for the frames-of-reference and coordinating-systems of relativity. And quiescent energy would play the part of the relativist 'systems of inertia.'

This ether-scheme also follows relativity theory in making no attempt to establish absolute localization or absolute velocity, differing in this from nineteenth-century schemes.

No doubt we could imagine anywhere in the ether a notional fixed point-instant; but it would serve no purpose. For the moment we tried to measure movements or time-intervals from it we should find that it did not remain fixed, in relation to the universe as a whole. A year later—or a second later—its location would be different. It would be fixed only with reference to the measurements we had ourselves chosen to make. That is to say, our notional point-instant would have only a relative location after all, and not the absolute location that we had tried to give it. As Professor Max Born says: "Relativity showed that the ether does not share with ordinary matter the property of 'localization': you cannot say 'here I am'; there is no physical way of identifying a point in the ether, as you would recognize a point in running water by a little mark, a particle of dust." In this the present scheme concurs.

On the other hand it would dissent from a statement such as the following, which appears in the book by Einstein and Infeld already quoted: "By far the greatest part of energy is concentrated in matter; but the field surrounding the particle also represents energy, though in incomparably smaller quantity." We should say the opposite.

If the proposition were accepted, some changes in terminology would necessarily follow. We would no longer speak of energy being conveyed or transferred, or being expended or stored, but only of its being active or quiescent. We would not say that a material object possesses energy, but that energy is active where the object is. And we would not say that a particle carries energy, but that energy carries the particle.

4

This last principle—that particles do not spontaneously move themselves in relation to their environment, but *are moved by* extraneous forces—may help when we try to deal with the difficult problem of waves and particles.

The nature of the problem has been clearly and briefly stated by Professor Henry Semat in his *Introduction to Atomic Physics.* He says: "The results of the experiments on the Compton effect leave no doubt that, in its interaction with matter, radiant energy behaves as though it were composed of particles. A similar behaviour was observed in the photo-electric effect. It will be shown later that in the processes of emission and absorption light behaves as though it consists of corpuscles. But the phenomena of interference and diffraction can be explained only on the hypothesis that radiant energy is propagated as a wave motion. We are thus led to the conclusion that radiant energy exhibits a dual character, that of a wave and that of a corpuscle." Semat also quotes L. de Broglie, who, he says, was led by considerations based upon the special theory of relativity and upon the quantum theory, to advance the hypothesis that "the dual character, wave and particle, should not be confined to radiation alone, but should also be exhibited by all the fundamental entities of physics. On this hypothesis, electrons, protons, atoms and molecules should have some type of wave motion associated with them." He adds that "results of . . . experiments confirm de Broglie's hypothesis that there is a wave motion associated with every moving electron." Schrödinger says: "A vast amount of experimental evidence clinches the conviction that wave characteristics and particle characteristics are never encountered singly, but always in union; they form different aspects of the same phenomenon, and indeed of all physical phenomena." Richtmyer and Kennard say that "Even molecules should exhibit wave properties under suitable conditions, according to the new theory. This, too, has been verified by experiment."

The conception of a single entity with a dual character, at once wave and particle, is hard to understand. It is not made the easier by the suggestion, usually advanced in this connection, that these are two 'aspects' of the same phenomenon. What is meant by the word Aspects? Is it more than an escape word, signifying nothing in itself? It recalls the specious saying that "truth has many facets," which conveniently allows anyone to accept at the same time two opposite views on any subject.

The scheme offered here would allow us to take into consideration three factors:

First, we conceive that a particle is one thing and its relative motion is another. Unless a particle is in motion, it is not perceptible to observation; and if it is in motion, there must be a wave sequence to carry it. Waves are "always associated with" a moving particle because, if they were not, it would not be moving.

Secondly, we conceive that new particles are continually being brought into being as a normal process of the universe. It appears that this may sometimes occur when an ether wave-series is obstructed. The activating impulse persists but is concentrated into particles. An analogy would be seen in seawaves falling on a shore and producing a spray of discrete drops, each drop having acquired an inner cohesion of its own. The drops are thrown forward in lines perpendicular to the wave-front, and with an initial velocity corresponding with the velocity of the wave.[1]

[1] Sir John Cockroft, the Director of the great Atomic Energy Research Establishment at Harwell, spoke as follows (in an address

Whittaker says on this subject: "According to theory, any field should give rise to a particle in the same way as the field considered in the wave-theory of light, namely, the electromagnetic field, gives rise to the photon." He adds, "There should therefore be a particle corresponding to the gravitational field. Of this nothing is known." (This theoretical particle has been designated a 'graviton.')

A particle may be emitted from an atom, or from a wave-front, with a high initial velocity, approximating to that of light. This high velocity, although combined with a very small mass, may suffice to give the particle a momentum that will cause an impact on the quiescent ether strong enough to effect a continuing activation. The particle will then travel forward so long as the process lasts.

Thirdly, we may also suppose that a particle, if obstructed, may be broken up, and the impulse persist in the form of waves.

Seeking an explanation of the mix-up of waves and particles revealed by many experiments, we may perhaps, then, find a line of inquiry by trying to disentangle those three possible factors: a moving particle needing waves to make it move; a wave-sequence, in certain circumstances, producing jets of particles; particles, in certain circumstances, breaking up into waves.

to the Parliamentary and Scientific Committee, reported in *The Times* of February 21, 1951): "They had developed at Harwell a new kind of atomic particle accelerator in which electrons were made to surf-ride in front of an electric wave which travelled down a hollow tube. The wave travelled faster and faster and so did the electrons." This corresponds somewhat closely with the process suggested here.

5

It is evident that wave-radiations are able to carry particles, also atoms, and apparently molecules. But objects of gross matter seem to need a different kind of ether activity—a motor action—to bear them along, and they attain only a much lower range of velocities.

We conceive that particles are formed in the quiescent ether, through causes unknown, as well as being emitted at a high velocity. In that case it may be supposed that they would as a rule be motionless, in relation to their environment. They would be capable, no doubt, of combining with others to form atoms, and the atoms of combining to form molecules. These would constitute the free components, mingling with the inter-stellar dust, that have been detected.

A particle may have been given a momentum sufficient to bring its impact above the minimum needed to start, or to maintain, a wave-activation, but only just above. In that case none of the wave-spheres might be completed. There would then come into existence a wave-sequence, not of spheres, but of portions of spheres. Would this be the cause of "the wavelets scattered by free electrons"—a longitudinal series of lateral wavelets—which have been revealed in recent years?

6

It is wonderful how much has been discovered by physicists about this ether world (although they have denied it that name) which underlies our own—so close in proximity but in scale so remote. We find that it is a very complicated world. Clearly we are only at the beginning of the task of unravelling the many elements that, to us, seem entangled and confused. Yet nature is not confused. One by one we are finding out the rules through which has been evolved the orderly and rational universe of which we are part.

If the physics of the future recognizes these basic principles—first, that matter consists of particles (this is already established); second, that energy exists in a state of inertia as well as in a state of activity; and third, that gravity is caused by an electromagnetic radiation from a center which evokes a motor response from the side of the object—then one welcome consequence will follow. In order to explain certain of its phenomena, physics will no longer need to have recourse to the figment of 'potential energy of position.'

For example, if there is a lake in the mountains dammed up to serve as reservoir for a hydroelectric powerhouse in the plain below, we are assured that the water in it 'possesses potential energy,' which can be 'liberated' and 'made available' to drive the engines and generators.

Or suppose that I have a grandfather-clock and wind up the weights and set the pendulum swinging: I shall be told that the energy I have expended is not lost, but is stored up in the weights, and is gradually used in moving the pendulum and the clockwork. That it is the same dose of energy is held to be proved by the fact that, if the amount of work done by me is measured and also the work done by the clock mechanism, they will be found to be the same: it is merely the form that has been changed; first from kinetic energy to potential, and afterwards from potential back to kinetic.

But such explanations are open to challenge and an alternative may be offered.

As to the reservoir above the hydroelectric powerhouse, the situation is that the body of water is being incessantly pulled down by the earth's gravity—as would usually be said; or, as we would say here, is being pushed down by ether action evoked by the earth's gravital radiation. It is therefore pressing all the time against the sand and earth and rock underneath, which dynamically resists it. When the sluice is opened the water at that point becomes free to move: it pours down the pipes or channel, being progressively accelerated as it falls; and it does work upon the turbines, proportional to its volume and the height of its fall.

If, after passing beyond the power-house, the water is stored in a second reservoir, for supplying some town, it can no longer do work of that kind. But that is not because the water in the upper reservoir had been endowed with a store of 'potential energy,' which had been 'spent' on the way down in producing electric current, so that the second reservoir has none. It is merely because the water in the reservoir among the mountains had been set free to move downwards, in obedience to the continuous pressure upon it; while the water in the reservoir below has no room for such movement.

To this it may be answered that so far no account has been taken of the original position of the water in the upper reservoir. It is here, we are told, that the rays of the sun come into the matter. It was their energy which had evaporated the water from the surface of the sea and, as it is colloquially said, sucked it up into the cloud strata, to be discharged again as rain or snow on the hill-tops. Hence the phenomenon of its 'potential energy of position.'

Let us examine a little more closely the meaning of the expression 'sucked up.' Evidently what has happened is that the radiation of heat-waves by the sun, first, has spread apart the water-molecules at the surface of the sea, causing fewer of them to occupy the same space, and thus changing them from a liquid state into vapor that is less heavy. Secondly, the heat has similarly expanded the atoms and molecules in the layer of air resting on the surface of the water, thereby making it lighter than the colder and more condensed air above. The consequence is that this colder air, pressed down by the effects of the earth's gravity, has sunk, and the hot air has risen, carrying up the water-vapor mixed with it, which will afterwards be condensed into cloud.

The process is exactly the same as that which causes a balloon full of hydrogen to rise above the heavier atmosphere of oxygen and nitrogen; or a fire in a grate to create a draught up the chimney; or, let us say, a cork released at the bottom of a tank to rise to the surface. We might as correctly describe each of these events by saying that the heavier air has flowed down under the balloon containing a lighter gas; that the colder and heavier air of the room has rushed in from around the grate to push the heated air up the chimney; that the water has pressed its way under the cork and lifted it to the surface. There is no question of the sun's rays, or anything else, 'sucking up' the balloon, the draught of air or the cork. In the case we are considering, the sun's heat has evaporated the top layer of the liquid sea, and has also made the adjacent layer of air lighter than the air above it; but it has done no more than that. The rest is merely an ordinary gravity effect, such as we see invariably in the positional relations between lighter and heavier objects or gases, if they are free to move. So the notion of a 'suction of energy' is no more than an illusion, and the 'storing of potential energy' —in the clouds, or on a hill-top, or anywhere else—merely a figment.

The same applies in the example of the clock-weights. When the weights are resting at their lowest point they are being pressed down incessantly by gravity. When I wind them up, the amount of work that I do is just the amount needed to counter and overcome the effect of gravity, and is therefore approximately equal to it. When they reach their highest point, one process is completed. If I do not start the clock again nothing more may happen. The clock may be left, wound up but not working, for any period. If ultimately I set the pendulum swinging, I start a second process. The amount of gravital force which then gradually pushes the weights down, is necessarily the same in its total as the amount of muscular force which was required at the beginning in order to raise the same weights the same distance.

We have thus been considering two separate occasions. On the first, gravity is at work countered by muscular effort. On the second, gravity is still at work, this time countered by the resistance of the swinging pendulum and the clock mechanism. Whether the force is gravity or some kind of counter-gravity, and whether the resultant movement of the weights is upward or downward, makes no difference to the amounts of the forces engaged.

There is therefore no need to imagine that, during the time interval between the two processes, there must be a particular dose of energy lying about somewhere; and that we are called upon to give to this "airy nothing a local habitation and a name"—a location 'in' the weights, and the name 'potential energy.'

7

Physicists are becoming conscious of the doubtful validity of these unobservables. A later passage in the encyclopaedia that I have quoted strikes a note of scepticism. Whittaker, in a paragraph already referred to, spoke of "hidden structures which are postulated in order to account for observable effects, and, in particular, all localizations of potential energy." Hidden structures may sometimes prove not so different from the 'occult qualities' of the Schoolmen.

At one time physics favored an hypothesis of a fluid called caloric to account for combustion and incandescence. At another time—in the eighteenth century and early nineteenth—it was the 'Phlogistic theory' that held the field: a specific physical constituent of matter was imagined, named 'phlogiston,' that was supposed to be given off in combustion as light and heat; and for this strong empirical arguments could be adduced.

These ideas have been abandoned, but 'potential energy of position' survives into the present-day world as a last example of the same series. Engineers may indeed continue to find the term technically useful in measurement and calculation. But ought modern theoretical physics still to give it acceptance, and teach it to the students? [2]

[2] See note in *References and Notes*, page 169.

VI. The Theory of the Expanding Universe

1

My argument is completed. But I add another section, on a subject detached from the rest, because the scheme put forward in this essay may have a bearing upon it. It is the theory, at present accepted by most physicists, that the universe is continuously and rapidly expanding, and that the greater the distance of the nebulae from one another, the greater is the velocity of the expansion.

Although now usually accepted, this theory cannot yet be regarded as established. It was propounded as a consequence of the discovery that lines in the spectra of distant nebulae, compared with the normal, are shifted towards the red, and that the amount of the shift varies directly with the distance. The observations and calculations of the American astronomer, Dr. Edwin Hubble, and his collaborators, provided the data out of which the theory arose, but Hubble himself has much doubt whether it is a correct interpretation. In his Oxford lectures published under the title *The Observational Approach to Cosmology,* he speaks of "the phenomena of red-shifts whose significance is still uncertain." He says that "alternative interpretations are possible. . . . Red-shifts are produced either in the nebulae, where the light originates, or in the intervening space through which the light travels. If the source is in the nebulae, then red-shifts are probably velocity-shifts and the nebulae are receding. If the source lies in the intervening space, the explanation of red-shifts is unknown but the nebulae are sensibly stationary." In that case, he says, "they represent some unknown reaction between the light and the medium through which it travels." The Expansion Theory itself he regards as leading to conclusions that are "rather startling" and "strange and dubious." He ends by saying that the results of the exploration "are a definite step in the observational approach to cosmology. . . . But the essential clue, the interpretation of red-shifts must still be unravelled. The former sense of certainty has faded and the clue stands forth as a problem for investigation."

Dr. Einstein, in the concluding paragraphs of *Relativity: The Special and the General Theory,* refers to the calculations as to the age of the universe to which the Expansion Theory has given rise, and says: "A few years later Hubble showed by a special investigation of the extra-galactic nebulae ('milky ways') that the emitted spectral lines showed a red-shift which increased regularly with the distance of the nebulae. This can be interpreted according to our present knowledge only in the sense of Doppler's principle as an expansive motion of the system of stars in the large—as required by the field equations of gravitation according to Friedman. Hubble's discovery can, therefore, be considered to some extent as a confirmation of the theory. There does arise, however, a strange difficulty. The interpretation of the galactic line-shift discovered by Hubble as expansion (which can hardly be doubted from a theoretical point of view), leads to an origin of expansion which lies 'only' about 10^9 years ago, while physical astronomy makes it appear likely that the development of individual stars and systems of stars takes considerably longer. It is in no way known how this incongruency is to be overcome."

Although Sir Arthur Eddington, in his book *The Expanding Universe,* accepts a "general scattering apart" as the proper inference from the facts as ascertained, he adds, "I do not wish to insist on these facts dogmatically. It is granted that there is a possibility of error and misinterpretation. The survey is just beginning, and things may appear in a different light as it proceeds."

In his standard text-book on *Physical Optics,* R. W. Wood wrote: "Astrophysicists are not quite certain at the present time [1933] as to whether these enormous line-shifts represent real velocities, or are due to some other cause as yet undetermined." And the most recent writer on this subject, Dr. G. J. Whitrow, says that "The whole problem bristles with complications, although in time new criteria may help to resolve them" and that meanwhile "the ultimate verdict" has not been given.

In view of these doubts, widespread and persisting among scientists of high authority, we may be allowed to regard the whole theory of an expanding universe as still open to question.

2

Let me recall what has been said in earlier sections. When radiation is emitted it does not arrive at any destination at the moment of the emission, but after a time interval. Light emitted from the sun arrives at the earth, and can produce an effect on a human eye, or on the plate of an astronomer's camera, after an interval of about eight minutes. During that time, and across that distance, some system of transmission must be operating. And the phenomenon is not a single event, beginning at the sun and ending at the earth, because it can be stopped at any point in the journey by the interposition of a material object. It must therefore be a process, divisible into a succession of events.

The scheme suggested in this essay accepts the theory that the process is initiated by atomic oscillations in the sun and that the transmission has the pattern of a continuous sequence of spherical waves. But it contends that a pattern must presuppose the existence of something else as the subject of the patterning. And if the phenomena produced are physically real, that something must also be physically real. The inference is drawn that this something else must be the Energy, which in various forms is a familiar part of our experience. The waves themselves are conceived to be a succession of transformations of energy from a quiescent state into an active state, followed by relapses into quiescence. Each individual wave is, first, a separate activation of a layer of quiescent energy; causing, secondly, an impact on the surrounding sphere of quiescent energy, which is thereby activated; followed, thirdly, by a return to quiescence.

It is conceived also that these spheres expand as they travel, and that, with the increase in size, the strength of the impact at any point-instant is diminished. (If that were not so, the power of the radiation would remain the same throughout the journey: the temperature at the earth's orbit, for instance, would be the same as at the sun's surface; and this planet—the other planets also—could not exist as solid bodies.) This change in the strength of the impacts, being consequent upon the increase in the size of the spheres, must be in proportion to that increase. Since, mathematically, the area of the surface of any sphere increases with the square of its radius, the strength of the impact in a sequence of expanding spheres must diminish in that ratio.

3

Turning now to the specific question of the red-shifts and an expansion of the universe, it is tacitly assumed that this change in the size of the spheres and in the strength of any impact that there may be, is the only change that occurs in the course of the transmission. But no ground can be given for such an assumption. It may well be that there is some other variation, the result of an entirely different cause. The strength of the impact transmitted by any one layer of energy to the next may not only be less than that of the impact received because of its being distributed over a slightly larger area; it may be further lessened by the effort itself. We can conceive that the actual process, wave by wave, of transformation from quiescence to activity and back again may involve an additional loss of impetus.

In that case an element of 'drag' would come in, its effect analogous to friction in mechanics. The variation would certainly be far too small to be detected by direct observation. But repeated several hundreds of millions of millions of times in a second—the scale of the frequencies of the light-waves; and—in spectra from the distant galaxies—this having been continued for hundreds of millions of years, in the end the effect of the drag might be great. It might well amount to the 13 per cent of the original impetus, which is the estimated shift in the spectra of the farthest galaxies observable in the most powerful telescopes of the present day.

4

Such a factor would affect all the color-waves equally, and would extend also to the neighboring radiation in the ultra-violet and infra-red. And its effect would increase cumulatively with the distance travelled.

Since all these waves move with the same velocity, the drag could operate only by lessening their frequency. Their movement would be hindered. The number of waves transmitted in a millionth of a second would become less and less, very slightly, as the journey went on. Velocity remaining constant, a smaller frequency means a correspondingly greater wave-length.

The mechanism, then, of such a process might be pictured as follows. All the wave-lengths in a packet of light-radiation—comprising the ultra-violet, the visible colored band, and the infra-red—would be infinitesimally lengthened with each successive wave, every sort of wave-length being modified equally. The effect would become perceptible only when this had been repeated a vast number of times. The result would be that, in the course of a journey from a distant galaxy to the solar system, waves which had started as ultra-violet would arrive as violet; violet would have become blue; blue would be green; and so on to orange, which would be red, and red which would be infra-red. That is to say, there would be an 'all-together' shift of the whole spectrum towards the region of the longer wave-lengths. The appearance of the visible part of the spectrum, however, would not be affected. What it had gained through the encroachment of the ultra-violet at one end it would lose through an equal expansion into the infra-red at the other. The relative position of the colors among themselves would remain unchanged.[1]

[1] One of the scientists who have read this section in draft writes: "The question might be raised: what becomes of the lost energy? In a material medium behaving similarly it would be transformed into heat in the medium; in an expanding universe it would occupy the larger space being made available; but on your theory it is not clear what happens to it, and I think a physicist would want to know that." This raises the general question of the principle of Conservation of Energy in relation to the present scheme, which has been considered in the previous section. We would no longer speak of "losing energy." What we suppose to happen would be that, with each successive wave, the impact would be weakened in a minute degree, and the amount of quiescent energy brought into activity would be diminished.

5

If that had been the whole picture the shift might not have been detected. It is remarkable that the faint spectra of distant nebulae have been obtained at all, and the shift would have been extremely difficult to discover but for the existence of dark lines in these spectra similar to those occurring in the spectra of the sun and many stars. These dark lines occur in the places where in laboratory spectra we find bright lines representing the various elements, *e.g.*, calcium. This absence of calcium light in stellar spectra is not due to a lack of that element in the composition of the stars themselves. It is attributed to a special quality in their gaseous atmospheres. This has the effect of singling out and absorbing the waves in the light-packets which emanate from calcium atoms in the incandescent star, and the light goes on without them. When this light is analysed in the spectroscope and presented in a colored band, the calcium lines can be identified by their position among the rest and are found to be dark instead of bright, as in spectra produced in terrestrial laboratories. It is the fact that in the nebular spectra these are shifted, and in proportion to distance, which leads to the conclusion that the neighboring lines on each side, and the colored spectrum as a whole, must have shifted. And this conclusion cannot be gainsaid.

6

The speculation that is submitted here would offer a possible interpretation of these facts other than that now usually accepted. We conceive radiation to be a process of continuous activation of quiescent energy and relapse, producing a succession of waves; and that each such transformation may involve an infinitesimal loss of impetus. This drag would produce a very slight lessening of frequency and consequently an equivalent increase of wavelength. But the phenomenon of the so-called red-shift is, we know, nothing else than such an all-round increase in the wave-lengths of the radiation.

If this is so, we are confronted with two quite different phenomena which ought not to be confused together. There is, first, the red-shift, discovered by Doppler, caused by the ascertained motion of a star when it is along the line of sight of the observer: it is often compared to the change in the pitch of the whistle of a railway-engine when the train is approaching or receding. This is undoubtedly a velocity effect. Whether we accept the theory of a general recession and expansion or not, it is to be expected that, in a universe containing immense numbers of moving stars and galaxies, at any time some will be moving directly towards an observer situated on any one of them and some directly away. But these relatively few special cases cannot of themselves give ground for an all-embracing hypothesis of a "general scattering."

Secondly, we have the ascertained fact of a so-called red-shift, proportionate to distance, in the spectra of distant nebulae. This is found to be nothing else than a general gradual lengthening in the wave-lengths of the radiation. We suggest that this need not be a velocity effect like the other, but may be the consequence of a characteristic feature, hitherto unidentified, in the mechanism of the radiation itself.

Hubble offered us two alternatives—either the red-shifts are produced in the nebulae, in which case, he said, the nebulae are probably receding; or else they are produced in the intervening space, in which case the nebulae are "sensibly stationary." If we were able to accept the second alternative, cosmology would be freed from a theory which this leading authority regards as "strange and dubious"; and which Einstein tells us leads to a direct contradiction, so far unresolved, with conclusions previously reached in other departments of astrophysics.

Postscript

This essay has not attempted to discuss the question of Matter and Mind. It has taken as its subject, not the whole of reality, but only physical reality. It has supported the view that an energic ether exists, and that it is the sole *material* constituent of the universe, not that it is the sole constituent. But I cannot conclude without expressing my own conviction that there is another—a mental element—which may be fundamentally the same as the vital element—also existent.

1

The first discoverers of the monuments, inscriptions and manuscripts of ancient Egypt found themselves in presence of what was, without question, a bygone civilization. Some features in it they could appreciate at once; but its ideas, its systems of religion, ethics, law, they could not understand—because they could not read its language. The Rosetta Stone before long gave a clue; the lost alphabets were reconstituted, the writings were deciphered, and the civilization revealed. Man, conscious of himself and of nature around him, knows likewise that he is in presence of an orderly system of immense complexity. He hears incessant voices—

all this mighty sum
Of things forever speaking.

But it speaks a language he does not know—the language of phenomena. He has no Rosetta Stone. As best he may, he must first try to distinguish the words, then to translate them into his own speech: afterwards, perhaps, he will be able to understand something of the meaning of it all.

This first task is the function of science. Laboriously, painfully, science has succeeded in distinguishing some of the words in this language of phenomena; it applies to them terms taken from our own vocabulary. The terms are such as gravity, electricity, magnetism, wave, atom, light, heat, sound. Every few years we decipher and translate a few more of the words—the latest, radioactivity, particle, quantum.

Hitherto the successes of science have been mainly on the material side, in the spheres belonging to physics and chemistry. We perceive indeed that nature has other aspects; to them too we have given names. We call them Life and Mind. But of these we have as yet no knowledge comparable to that which we have so industriously gathered with regard to matter. Indeed those two words convey no definite meanings at all. We observe events that we can describe only as consequences of vital or mental processes: we cannot say what those processes are, or how they are brought about. We cannot analyse the events into prior events that have caused them as we can analyse material objects. We do not even know whether

Life and Mind are two distinct elements in the universe, or are different manifestations of a single factor.

On the mental aspect I have written elsewhere, though not on the relations between mind and life. In these final pages I can do no more than offer, very briefly, the gist of the conclusions then presented.[1]

2

If, as philosophers, we try "to keep our eye on the object," we see so fundamental a difference between the activities of the mind and those that produce material phenomena that it is hard to understand how the reality of that division can be doubted or disputed. Consider a mathematician thinking out the solution of a problem, a novelist beginning his next chapter, a violinist playing a piece from memory: and then compare the action of what Whitehead called the 'senseless agencies'—atoms combining to form molecules, water freezing or boiling, a needle jumping to a magnet, the wind swaying the trees, the moon circling round the earth or the earth round the sun. The difference goes deep. Watch a chess-player cogitating for half an hour whether to move his queen here or his pawn there; at last stretching out his hand and doing the one or the other. The physiologist may describe the nervous and muscular mechanism which operates the movement, but not the process which has decided the choice. The chess-player himself is evidently of a different order from the chess-board and the pieces: in him

[1] For references see *References and Notes*, page 169.

there is some activity going on which is not material; in them there is not. Intellectual creativity, the power of choice, are of a different order from chemical and electrical reactions.

We cannot therefore accept the view of materialist scientists that in the end all phenomena can be resolved into atomic or electric attractions and repulsions. To speak of these higher activities of human, or other, organisms being the product of 'compound nervous reflexes' does not carry us one inch nearer to an explanation.

Nor, on the other hand, can we accept the view of those idealist philosophers who hold that, at bottom, the mental conceptions are the only reality. It is easy to say that, when we philosophize, we are dealing with ideas, and that therefore nothing exists—for philosophy—except a world of ideas. Some deduce from this that we can do no more than concentrate on logical analysis, classification into categories, the meanings of words. This is important, no doubt; but it is dealing with means, not with ends. When we do this we are studying, not the things that are to be investigated, but only our own tools of investigation. The brushes, paints, and canvas are important to the artist: they condition his work; but it is the picture that we want, the ideas it conveys, the thoughts and emotions it evokes, that we care about.

The two views—materialist and idealist—contradict one another; and, it seems, plain fact contradicts both.

3

The alternative is to accept a duality in nature. The subjects dealt with by physics and chemistry (other than biophysics and biochemistry) are one thing; the subjects dealt with by psychology, aesthetics, sociology, ethics, religion are another. As Sir Charles Sherrington has said, "That our being should consist of *two* fundamental elements offers I suppose no greater inherent improbability than that it should rest on one only."

It is true that the word Fundamental is not to be applied too strictly. Mind and matter connect and interact: this is indisputable. It does not follow, however, that because they interact, they are the same thing. But it does follow that mind and matter must have some quality in common. This ultimate connection between psychics and physics seems, however, to be so far back in the order of nature that philosophy and science will be justified, for their own purposes, in treating the two as distinct.

An ether theory does not touch the problems of the mental factor in the universe. That vast field, still almost unexplored, remains a challenge to the inquiring spirit of man—never resting.

January, 1949–*August,* 1950.

Letter from Dr. Albert Einstein

Princeton, New Jersey, U.S.A.,
October 13th, 1950

Dear Herbert Samuel:

Your book has interested me very much. It is for me a new illustration of the fact that the philosophic outlook has—under present circumstances—a strong influence on the views in physics. To show you this I have tried to formulate in as short as possible a way an outline of my own opinions concerning reality and truth in comparison to yours. I felt not able to formulate this in English but did it in German. . . .

[*The original German text is given on page 163. The translation has been made by Dr. F. H. Heinemann, whose help is gratefully acknowledged.*]

I have now read your book. What impressed me most favorably was your independence of mind which reveals itself in your criticism as well as in your proposals. You demand that physics should describe what is 'physically real.' If physicists attempt to manage with purely fictitious concepts like number, they cannot, you say, reach their goal. You have got the impression that contemporary physics is based on concepts somewhat analogous to the "smile of the absent cat."

In fact, however, the 'real' is in no way immediately given to us. Given to us are merely the data of our consciousness; and among these data only those form the material of science which allow of univocal linguistic expression. There is only one way from the data of consciousness to 'reality,' to wit, the way of conscious or unconscious intellectual construction, which proceeds completely free and arbitrarily. The most elementary concept in everyday thought, belonging to the sphere of the 'real,' is the concept of continually existing objects, like the table in my room. The table as such, however, is not given to me, but merely a complex of sensations is given to which I attribute the name and concept 'table.' This is a speculative method, based on intuition. In my opinion, it is of the greatest importance to be conscious of the fact that such a concept, like all other concepts, is of a speculative-constructive kind. Otherwise one cannot do justice to those concepts which in physics claim to describe reality, and one is in danger of being misled by the illusion that the 'real' of our daily experience 'exists really,' and that certain concepts of physics are 'mere ideas' separated from the 'real' by an unbridgeable gulf. In fact, however, positing the 'real' which exists independently of my sensations is the result of intellectual construction. We happen to put more trust in these constructions than in the interpretations which we are making with reference to our sensations. Thence arises our confidence in statements like these: "There were trees long before there was a creature able to perceive them."

These facts could be expressed in a paradox, namely that reality, as we know it, is exclusively composed of 'fancies.' Our trust or our confidence in our thoughts referring to reality is solely based on the fact, that these concepts and relations stand in a relation of 'correspondence' with our sensations. Therein the 'truth' of our statements is founded. Such it is in daily life and in science. If now in physics this correspondence or correlation between our concepts and our sensations becomes more and more indirect, we are not entitled to accuse this science of replacing reality by fancies. A criticism of this sort would only be justified if we were able to show that it is impossible to correlate the concepts of a specific theory in a satisfactory manner with our experience.

We are free to choose which elements we wish to apply in the construction of physical reality. The justification of our choice lies exclusively in our success. For example, Euclidean geometry, considered as a mathematical system, is a mere play with empty concepts (straight lines, planes, points, etc., are mere 'fancies'). If, however, one adds that the straight line be replaced by a rigid rod, geometry is transformed into a *physical theory.* A theorem, like that of Pythagoras, then gains a reference to reality. On the other hand, the simple correlation of Euclidean geometry is being lost, if one notices that the rods, which are empirically at our disposal, are not 'rigid.' But does this fact reveal Euclidean geometry to be a mere fancy? *No,* a rather complicated sort of co-ordination exists between geometrical theorems and rods (or, generally speaking, the external world) which takes into account elasticity, thermic expansion, etc. Thereby geometry regains physical significance. Geometry may be true or false, according to its ability to establish correct and verifiable relations between our experiences.

But now I hear you saying: "All right, but the real world exists, independent of the fact whether we have a theory about it or not." Such a statement has, in my opinion, no other meaning than the following, *i.e.*, "I *believe* that there exists a satisfactory theory based on the assumption of fictitious objects extended in spacetime and their regular relations." Such a belief is deeply ingrained in us, because it is practically indispensable as a basis of pre-scientific thought. Science accepts this belief, but transforms it radically, leaving it open in principle of what kind these elements are. Within Newton's system they were space, material points, and motion. Newton recognized with complete clarity that in his system space and time were just as real things as material points. For if one does not accept, besides material objects, space and time as real things, the law of inertia and the concept of acceleration lose all meaning. 'Accelerated' means nothing but 'accelerated in relation to space.'

Since the days of Faraday and Maxwell the conviction has established itself that 'mass' has to be replaced by 'field' as a basic element or brick for constructing 'reality.' For how should it be possible to reduce light, which can only be represented as a 'field,' to material elements in motion? This has been tried strenuously, but unsuccessfully and, in the end, the attempt had to be given up. The conviction of the non-existence of a 'stationary ether,' which followed from the special theory of relativity, was only the last step in this transition from the concept of 'mass' to that of 'field' as an elementary concept in physics, *i.e.*, as an irreducible conceptual element in the logical construction of 'reality.' Therefore, I think, it is not justified to regard mass as something 'real,' the field, however, as merely a 'fancy.' These are prejudices that spring from a primitive understanding of the concept of 'reality.'

The program of the field-theory has the great advantage that it makes a separate concept of space (as distinguished from space-content) superfluous. The space is then merely the four-dimensionality of the field, and no longer something existing in isolation. This is an achievement of the General Theory of Relativity which, so far, seems to have escaped the attention of the physicists.

As to those who regard contemporary quantum theory as a piece of knowledge which is final in principle, they waver in fact between two possible interpretations, namely:

1. There is a physical reality. Its laws, however, do not allow of any other than statistical expression.

2. There is nothing at all which corresponds to a physical situation. Merely probabilities 'exist' and may be observed.

We both agree on this point: we regard these two interpretations with disbelief and we believe in the possibility of a theory which is able to give a complete description of reality, the laws of which establish relations between the things themselves and not merely between their probabilities.

But I do not think that this belief of contemporary

physicists is *philosophically* refutable. For in my opinion an intellectual resignation cannot be refuted as being logically impossible. Here I simply put my trust in my intuition.

Letter from Dr. Albert Einstein

Princeton, New Jersey, U.S.A.,
October 11th, 1950

Ich habe nun Ihr Buch gelesen. Was mich dabei hauptsächlich gefreut hat, ist Ihre intellektuelle Unabhängigkeit. Diese zeigt sich sowohl in Ihrer Kritik als auch in Ihren Vorschlägen.

Sie verlangen: die Physik hat das zu beschreiben, was physikalisch real ist. Wenn sie versucht, mit rein fiktiven Begriffen auszukommen, wie Zahlen, dann könne sie ihr Ziel nicht erreichen. Sie haben den Eindruck, dass die gegenwärtige Physik sich auf Begriffe stütze, die dem 'smile of the absent cat' einigermassen analog sind.

Nun ist es aber so, dass das 'Reale' uns in keiner Weise unmittelbar gegeben ist, sondern nur Erlebnisse menschlicher Geschöpfe sind uns gegeben. Und von diesen Erlebnissen kommen für die Wissenschaft nur solche als Material in Betracht, die sich eindeutig sprachlich fixieren lassen. Von den Erlebnissen zu der 'Realität' gibt es aber nur den Weg der intellektuellen Konstruktion (bewusst oder unbewusst), die—rein logisch betrachtet—völlig frei und willkürlich verfährt. Der elementarste Begriff im Alltags-Denken, der der Sphäre des 'Realen' angehört, ist der Begriff von dauernd existierenden Gegenständen, wie der Tisch in meinem Zimmer. Der Tisch als solcher ist mir aber nicht gegeben, sondern ein Inbegriff von einzelnen Erlebnissen, denen der Begriff 'Tisch' zugeordnet wird. Es ist eine intuitiv entwickelte spekulative Methode. Dass so ein Begriff—wie alle anderen Begriffe—, obwohl er sich auf Erlebnisse bezieht, spekulativ-konstruktiven Charakter hat, dieses Umstandes sich lebhaft bewusst zu sein, ist nach meiner Meinung sehr wesentlich, wenn man den Begriffen gerecht werden will, welche, in der Physik darauf Anspruch machen, das Physikalisch-Reale zu beschreiben. Sonst verfällt man leicht auf die Idee: Das 'Reale' im täglichen Leben, das 'existiert wirklich,' aber gewisse physikalische Begriffe sind 'blosse Ideen,' die von dem 'Realen' durch einen unüberbrückbaren Abgrund getrennt sind. In Wahrheit ist die Setzung des 'Realen,' unabhängig von meinem Erlebnis Existierenden ein Inbegriff von gedanklichen Konstruktionen, denen wir aber mehr intellektuelles Vertrauen entgegenbringen, als den Interpretationen, welche unseren einzelnen Erlebnissen entsprechen. Daher das Vertrauen, das wir Sätzen entgegenbringen wie: Es hat Bäume gegeben, bevor ein Geschöpf sie wahrnehmen konnte.

Man kann also paradox sagen: Die Realität, wie wir sie kennen, besteht ausschliesslich aus 'Hirngespinsten.' Unser Vertrauen in das auf die 'Realität' bezügliche Gedankengut beruht allein darauf, dass sich jene Begriffe und Relationen mit unseren Erlebnissen in einer Relation des 'Entsprechens' befinden; darin allein liegt die 'Wahrheit' unserer Aussagen begründet. So ist es im Alltagsleben und in der Wissenschaft. Wenn nun in der Physik das Entsprechen zwischen dem Begrifflichen und Erlebbaren immer indirekter wird, so dürfen wir sie nicht einfach beschuldigen, dass sie die Realität durch Hirngespinste ersetzen wolle. Wir dürfen eine solche Kritik nur dann vorbringen, wenn wir zeigen, dass die Begriffswelt in einer bestimmten Theorie mit den Erfahrungen nicht in der zu fordernden Weise verknüpfbar ist.

Es liegt also in unserer Wahl, was wir als Elemente in der Konstruktion der physikalischen Realität verwenden wollen. Die Berechtigung der Wahl liegt ausschliesslich im Erfolg.

Beispiel: Die euklidische Geometrie ist–als mathematisches System betrachtet–ein Spiel mit leeren Begriffen (Gerade Linien, Ebenen, Punkte, Strecken sind blosse 'Hirngespinste'). Wenn man aber hinzufügt: Die Strecke lässt sich durch einen (starren) Stab ersetzen, dann wird die Geometrie eine *physikalische Theorie.* Es enthält dann ein Satz wie, zum Beispiel, der pythagoreische Satz einen Realgehalt. Die einfache Korrelation der euklidischen Geometrie geht verloren, wenn man bemerkt, dass die empirisch verfügbaren Stäbe nicht 'starr' sind. Wird dadurch die euklidische Geometrie zum blossen Hirngespinst? *Nein:* es gibt eine kompliziertere Art der Zuordnung der geometrischen Sätze zu Stäben (zur 'realen Welt' überhaupt), welche die Elastizität, thermische Ausdehnung etc. berücksichtigt. Dadurch erhält die Geometrie wieder physikalischen Sinn; sie kann wahr oder falsch sein, je nachdem sie dazu geeignet ist, zutrefende prüfbare Beziehungen zwischen Erfahrungen herzustellen.

Nun höre ich Sie sagen: 'Schon gut, aber die reale Aussenwelt existiert, unabhängig davon, ob wir eine Theorie über sie haben oder nicht.' Eine solche Aussage hat nach meiner Meinung keinen andern Sinn als den:

Ich *glaube,* es gibt eine brauchbare Theorie die sich auf die Einführung irgend welcher fingierter raum-zeitlich ausgedehnter Dinge und deren gesetzlicher Relationen stützt. Dieser Glaube sitzt fest in uns, weil er als Basis des vorwissenschaftlichen Denkens praktisch unentbehrlich ist. Diesen Glauben übernimmt die Wissenschaft, modifiziert ihn aber in drastischer Weise dadurch, dass sie es im Prinzip weitgehend offen lässt, von welcher Art diese begrifflichen Elemente seien. Im Bereich des Newtonschen Systems waren es Raum, materialle Punkte und Bewegung. Newton erkannte mit voller Klarheit, dass Raum und Zeit vor seinem System ebenso reale Dinge waren wie die materiellen Punkte. Wenn man nämlich neben den materiellen Dingen nicht auch Raum und Zeit als reale Dinge auffasst, dann verliert das Trägheitsprinzip und der Beschleunigungs-Begriff jeden Sinn als real. 'Beschleungit' bedeutet eben 'beschleunigt inbezug auf den Raum.'

Seit Faraday und Maxwell hat sich die Ueberzeugung festgesetzt, dass als elementare begriffliche Bausteine der Realität die Massen durch Felder ersetzt werden müssen. Denn wie sollte das nur als 'Feld' darstellbare Licht, das ohne Zweifel als 'reales Ding' aufzufassen ist, sich auf bewegliche Massen zurückführen lassen? Man bemühte sich krampfhaft ohne Erfolg und gab es endlich auf. Die aus der speziellen Relativitätstheorie resultierende Ueberzeugung von der Nicht-Existenz des 'ruhenden Aethers' war nur der letzte Schritt dieses gedanklichen Uebergangs von der 'Masse' zum 'Feld' als physikalischen Elementarbegriff, d.h. als irreducibles begriffliches Element der Gedanken-Konstruktion der 'Realität.'

Ich denke also, dass es nicht gerechtfertigt ist, in der

Masse etwas 'Wirkliches,' in dem Feld aber ein blosses 'Gedankending' zu sehen. Dies sind Vorurteile, die aus einer primitiven Auffassung des Begriffes 'Realität' entspringen.

Das Programm der Feldtheorie hat den grossen Vorteil, dass der selbständige Raumbegriff (neben dem 'Raum-Inhalt') entbehrlich wird. Der Raum ist dann nichts weiter als die Vier-Dimensionalität des Feldes, kein selbständig Existierendes. Dies ist es, was die allgemeine Relativitätstheorie leistet. (Es scheint, dass die Physiker dies immer noch nicht richtig begriffen haben.)

Was nun Diejenigen anlangt, die die gegenwärtige Quantentheorie als im Prinzip endgültige Erkenntnis ansehen, so schwanken sie zwischen zwei theoretischen Auffassungen hin und her:

1. Es gibt eine physikalische Realität. Sie lässt sich aber in ihren Gesetzlichkeiten nur statistisch darstellen.

2. Es gibt überhaupt nichts, was einer realen physikalischen Situation entspricht. Was 'existiert' sind nur Wahrscheinlichkeiten für den Fall der Beobachtung.

Wir beide stimmen darin überein, dass wir beiden Auffassungen ungläubig gegenüberstehen und an die Möglichkeit einer Theorie glauben, die eine vollständig darstellbare Realität annimmt, deren Gesetze Relationen zwischen den Dingen selbst und nicht nur zwischen deren Wahrscheinlichkeiten sind.

Ich halte aber die Meinung der gegenwärtigen Physiker nicht für *philosophisch* widerlegbar. Denn ein intellektueller Verzicht kann meiner Meinung nach nicht auf Grund logischen Denkens als unmöglich widerlegt werden. Ich vertraue hier einfach meiner Intuition.

References and Notes

Abbreviations: C.U.P.–Cambridge University Press
O.U.P.–Oxford University Press

PAGE

3 H. T. BUCKLE, *History of Civilisation* (O.U.P.).

5 R. W. EMERSON, *Essays:* On Nature, p. 452 (Macmillan & Co.).

6 A. N. WHITEHEAD, *Science and the Modern World,* p. 219 (C.U.P.).

A. N. WHITEHEAD, *Essays in Science and Philosophy,* p. 246 (Rider & Co., 1948).

9 F. K. RICHTMYER and E. H. KENNARD, *Introduction to Modern Physics,* pp. 50, 330 (McGraw-Hill Book Co., Inc., New York and London, 1947).

A. N. WHITEHEAD, *Essays,* pp. 83, 85.

12 A. N. WHITEHEAD, *Essays,* p. 246.

13 M. BORN, *Natural Philosophy of Cause and Chance,* pp. 125, 104 (Oxford, Clarendon Press).

14 SIR R. GREGORY, Introduction to C. D. Darlington, *The Conflict of Science and Society,* p. ix (Watts & Co.).

RICHTMYER and KENNARD, *Op. cit.,* p. 268.

15 SIR A. S. EDDINGTON, *The Expanding Universe,* p. 17 (C.U.P., 1933).

SIR E. WHITTAKER, *From Euclid to Eddington,* p. 84 (C.U.P.).

18 BERTRAND RUSSELL, *The Listener,* March 17, 1949.

20 M. BORN, *Op. cit.,* pp. 123, 121, 83, 103, 47, 122, 123.

21 The paragraphs on Causation and on Chance repeat to some extent what I have previously written in *Belief and Action: An Everyday Philosophy* (Cassell & Co.); *Creative Man and Other Addresses* (Cresset Press); *Report of Ninth International Congress of Philosophy,*

PAGE

Paris, 1937: Causalité et Déterminisme, Vol. 7, pp. 21-27 (Hermann et Cie, Paris).

J. S. MILL, *System of Logic,* Book III, Chap. V, §111, quo. by C. Lloyd Morgan in *Emergent Evolution,* p. 280 (Williams & Norgate, Ltd.).

A. N. WHITEHEAD, *Nature and Life,* p. 87 (C.U.P.).

26 A. J. TOYNBEE, *A Study of History,* V, p. 436 (O.U.P.).

27 Ptolemaic cosmogony: see SIR W. C. DAMPIER-WHETHAM, *A History of Science,* pp. 48-50 (C.U.P., 1930); C. SINGER, *A Short History of Science,* p. 86 (O.U.P., 1941); H. BUTTERFIELD, *The Origins of Modern Science, 1300-1800,* pp. 15-21 (G. Bell & Sons, Ltd., 1950).

28 R. W. EMERSON, *Essays:* On Circles.

A. EINSTEIN, quo. H. SAMUEL, *Philosophy and the Ordinary Man,* p. 15 (Kegan Paul, Trench, Trubner & Co., Ltd.) and *Belief and Action,* p. 299.

29 Quo. M. PLANCK, *Where Is Science Going?,* p. 202 (George Allen & Unwin, Ltd.); M. BORN, *Op. cit.,* pp. 122, 123.

30 M. PLANCK, *The Universe in the Light of Modern Physics,* pp. 47, 141-147 (George Allen & Unwin, Ltd.).

BERTRAND RUSSELL, *The Scientific Outlook,* pp. 109-110 (George Allen & Unwin, Ltd.).

33 JOHN BUCHAN (Lord Tweedsmuir), *The Causal and the Casual in History,* pp. 14, 16, 22, 28 (C.U.P.).

36 LESLIE STEPHEN, *English Thought in the 18th Century* (John Murray).

38 M. PLANCK, *Where Is Science Going?,* p. 145.

39 NIELS BOHR, *Atomic Theory and the Description of Nature,* p. 18 (O.U.P.).

40 SIR I. NEWTON, *Opticks,* p. 401 (Bell & Sons).

41 A. N. WHITEHEAD, *Essays,* p. 92.

A. EINSTEIN and L. INFELD, *The Evolution of Physics,* p. 291 (C.U.P.).

42 SIR I. NEWTON, from a letter quoted by Florian Cajori in Appendix to *Mathematical Principles,* p. 634 (C.U.P.).

PAGE

A. EINSTEIN, *The Theory of Relativity*, p. 63 (Methuen & Co., Ltd.).

M. BORN, *Op. cit.*, p. 123.

T. PRESTON, *The Theory of Light*, p. 14, 5th ed. (Macmillan & Co.).

43 Michelson-Morley. See R. W. WOOD, *Physical Optics*, pp. 817-827 (The Macmillan Company, New York).

44 SIR E. WHITTAKER, *Op. cit.*, p. 96.

46 A. N. WHITEHEAD, *Essays*, p. 171.

48 LORD CHERWELL (F. A. Lindemann), *The Physical Significance of the Quantum Theory*, p. 143 (Clarendon Press, Oxford).

49 LORD CHERWELL, *Op. cit.*, p. 109.

51 SIR E. WHITTAKER, *Op. cit.*, p. 121.

52 H. POINCARE, see *Ibid.*, p. 97.

53 SIR I. NEWTON, *Opticks*, p. 348 (C.U.P.).

LORD RAYLEIGH, *Life of J. J. Thomson*, p. 203 (C.U.P.).

57 SIR E. WHITTAKER, *Op. cit.*, pp. 134-5.

61 ". . . linear wave of light," R. W. WOOD, *Op. cit.*, p. 9. Inverse-Square Law: for a text-book account see T. Preston, *The Theory of Light*, p. 46. Also E. GRIMSEHL, *A Textbook of Physics*, Vol. IV, Optics, p. 23 (Blackie & Son, Ltd.).

62 ". . . a moving configuration," LORD CHERWELL, *Op. cit.*, p. 127.

64 ". . . a plane wave of light," R. W. WOOD, *Op. cit.*, p. 31.

65 DR. N. KEMMER, *The Times*, Sept. 6, 1949.

DR. J. R. OPPENHEIMER, *Life*, Oct. 10, 1949, p. 122.

66 Positrons, ANDRADE, *The Atom and Its Energy*, p. 45 (G. Bell & Sons, 1947).

67 "A Rosette," H. SEMAT, *Introduction to Atomic Physics*, p. 20 (Rinehart & Co., Inc., New York, and Chapman & Hall, Ltd., 1947).

68 Particles created and destroyed, *e.g.*, DR. KEMMER, in a letter. DR. E. SCHRÖDINGER says, "Indeed, electrons too are created and annihilated." *Endeavour*, July 1950, p. 114 (Imperial Chemical Industries, London, S.W.1).

References and Notes

PAGE

F. HOYLE, *The Nature of the Universe*, p. 105 (Basil Blackwell, Oxford, 1950).

73 M. PLANCK, *Scientific Autobiography and Other Papers*, p. 139 (Williams & Norgate). David and Goliath, *I Samuel*, 17:49.

84 ". . . ton of uranium," SIR J. COCKCROFT, *The Development and Future of Nuclear Energy*, p. 19 (Romanes Lecture, 1950, Clarendon Press, Oxford). SIR E. WHITTAKER, *Op. cit.*, p. 112.

89 SIR A. S. EDDINGTON, *Proceedings of the Royal Society*, Vol. 102, 1923, p. 281.

SIR E. WHITTAKER, *Op. cit.*, p. 81.

90 SIR I. NEWTON, see *Ibid.*, p. 67.

95 Diagrams of lines of force, GRIMSEHL, *Op. cit.*, Vol. III, p. 35.

98 A. EINSTEIN, *The Meaning of Relativity*, Fourth ed., p. 128 (Methuen & Co., Ltd., 1950).

104 Transformations: see GRIMSEHL, *Op. cit.*, p. 257, Vol. III, p. 523. SIR I. NEWTON, *Opticks*, p. 374.

107 GRIMSEHL, *Op. cit.*, Vol. IV, pp. 3, 11.

112 "The greater light . . ." *Genesis*, 1:16.

130 M. BORN, *Op. cit.*, p. 74.

EINSTEIN and INFELD, *Op. cit.*, p. 256.

131 "A material particle carries energy," see RICHTMYER and KENNARD, *Op. cit.*, p. 237.

H. SEMAT, *Op. cit.*, pp. 144, 153, 165.

132 RICHTMYER and KENNARD, July, 1950, p. 110. *Op. cit.*, p. 257. E. SCHRÖDINGER, *Endeavour*.

134 SIR E. WHITTAKER, *Op. cit.*, pp. 166, 179.

135 "Wavelets scattered . . . ," RICHTMYER and KENNARD, *Op. cit.*, p. 459.

140 *Van Nostrand Scientific Encyclopaedia* (Van Nostrand Company, Inc., New York).

". . . Airy nothing," SHAKESPEARE, *A Midsummer Night's Dream*, V, i, 7.

141 SIR E. WHITTAKER, *Op. cit.*, p. 84.

Through the courtesy of the Education Officer to the London County Council I have had an opportunity of

PAGE

examining some forty elementary and advanced text-books on physics that are now being used in the London schools. In those which deal directly with this point, such passages as the following are typical: "The energy which a body possesses as the result of its motion is called Kinetic Energy. A brick on the table has more energy than a brick on the floor, though both are stationary; for if the brick is allowed to fall from the table to the floor it can *do work* in doing so. Energy which a body possesses as a result of its position is called 'Potential Energy'" (F. Sherwood Taylor, *General Science for Schools,* Part I, p. 115. William Heinemann, Ltd.). "Energy is the name given to the capacity, or power, of doing work, and obviously anything which can produce motion possesses energy, *e.g.,* a wound watch-spring, when released, moves the cog-wheel system of a watch. Stored-up energy of this kind is called potential energy" (R. G. Shackel, *Concise School Physics,* p. 77. Longmans Green & Co.). "When we wind any clock, we put into it quickly a quantity of potential energy which afterwards comes out very slowly in working the clock" (E. N. da C. Andrade and Julian Huxley, *Things Around Us,* p. 91. Basil Blackwell, Oxford).

These quotations are not intended as in any way a criticism of the compilers of the text-books: they can do no other than present, in a shape suited to students, the facts, conclusions, and theories that are currently accepted by the general body of teachers of the science in this and other countries. But the extracts make it evident that physics is still teaching that "potential energy of position" is an actuality and not a myth; and would lead us to believe, for example, that any rock-boulder near the top of a mountain must "possess" more energy than a similar boulder at the bottom, because, if set rolling, it could in the technical sense "do work."

142 E. P. HUBBLE, *The Observational Approach to Cosmology,* pp. v, 31, 45, 30, 43, 65.

143 A. EINSTEIN, *Relativity: The Special and the General Theory,* p. 134.

144 SIR A. S. EDDINGTON, *Op. cit.,* p. 13.

R. W. WOOD, *Op. cit.,* p. 26.

PAGE

G. J. WHITROW, *The Structure of the Universe*, pp. 33, 35 (Hutchinson's University Library, 1949).

147 ". . . about 13 per cent," G. J. WHITROW, *Op. cit.*, p. 38.

150 ". . . whistle of railway-engine," SIR A. S. EDDINGTON, *Op. cit.*, p. 16; G. J. WHITROW, *Op. cit.*, p. 30.

153 "All this mighty sum . . ." W. WORDSWORTH, Expostulation and Reply.

154 VISCOUNT SAMUEL, *Belief and Action: An Everyday Philosophy*, Chap. 2: The Universe Around Us; and Appendix 3: Mind and Matter (Cassell & Co., Ltd., London, 1937. American edition published by The Bobbs-Merrill Company, Indianapolis and New York. Also in the Pelican edition, published by Penguin Books Ltd.; and Dutch translation *Grondslag en Opbouw*, published by H. P. Leopold, The Hague. The last two editions do not include the Appendices).

See also one of the concluding contributions in a symposium broadcast by the B.B.C. with the title *The Physical Basis of Mind*, published as a book by Basil Blackwell, Oxford.

156 SIR C. SHERRINGTON, *The Integrative Action of the Nervous System*, Foreword to 1947 edition, p. xxiv (C.U.P.).

INDEX

Index